BRICK BY BRICK

The Leading Edge guide to building your own home

Edited by
JACKIE SCHOFIELD

Foreword by
DR ROD HACKNEY

Leading Edge
press and publishing

DEDICATION: To Joyce and Eileen. To the Fawcetts and Katy for the escape route, and to Graeme Bowker for taking me out of the classroom to meet the Lady in Purple.

First published 1989 by Leading Edge Press and Publishing, The Old Chapel, Burtersett, Hawes, North Yorkshire, DL8 3PB.
Tel (096 97) 566

British Library Cataloguing in Publication Data

Brick by Brick
    1. Great Britain. Residences. Construction.
    — Amateurs' manuals
    I. Schofield, Jackie, <u>1961</u> —
    690'.8' 0941

    ISBN 0-948135-10-7

Design: JACKIE SCHOFIELD
Front cover and cartoons: FRAN ORFORD
Produced at Leading Edge on Apple Macintosh™ and Aldus PageMaker™
Printed and bound in Great Britain by H Shanley (Printers) Ltd, Bolton

The editor wishes to thank *Prestoplan Homes, Design and Materials, Rationalised Building Systems, Homesmith Consultants, Constructive Individuals,* and the *National and Provincial Building Society.*
Thanks also to SA, BA and ME for being so finicky and saying all the right things.

Contents

Editor's preface

The idea of learning how to build your own home from the pages of a book is an odd one. People have been building homes, however primitive, a lot longer than they have been reading manuscripts, and as most of us know of experienced, competent builders who have learnt their trade by word of mouth the text book approach may seem of little value.

But **Brick by Brick,** is not a text book. It has been compiled with the 'word of mouth' principle in mind. Contributors have been invited to share their experiences and make clear their views. As a non-tradeswoman keen to learn, I had an endless stream of questions to ask; as self-build experts and correspondents, they had an enormous amount of knowledge to impart.

Yet the best way to serve any sort of 'apprenticeship' is to listen to those who've been through it themselves. The individual case studies accompanying every chapter provide the opportunity to do this. Each self-builder — many of them with little, or no, previous experience — has his or her own story to tell, and it is hoped that these will encourage others to have a go.

The case histories — easily identified by the location map and grey background — come at the end of each chapter to illustrate points made. With the exception of self-builder Mike Eydmann who has written his own story, all case studies and unattributed chapters have been researched and written at Leading Edge by myself, Barbara Allen and Stan Abbott.

I would like to thank all who have helped in the research and production of the book — in particular, those companies and contributors who have allowed me to pester, and the self-builders whose anecdotes and experiences have taught me a lot and kept me amused.

Jackie Schofield
February 1989

Rod Hackney

Foreword

BY DR ROD HACKNEY
President of the Royal Institute of British Architects

The self-build movement has grown up gradually as a result of the need for people to exercise one of society's fundamental rights — that of building a shelter for the family. In the Third World, with over one billion people homeless, there is an obvious need for these people to be allowed the right of access to land and the means to secure reasonable building materials in order to provide such a shelter.

Many of those who are homeless in the world's largest cities have come from rural surroundings where, although there is abject poverty, there was a structure in which they could survive. The bright lights of the metropolis often beckoned, and only when it was too late did these new urban poor realise that to be poor in the city was a far greater problem than being poor in their traditional rural surroundings. There at least they had access to air and some means of sustenance from the products of the land.

Programmes of resettlement, self-help and community architecture in Caracas, Bogota, Lima, Djakarta and Colombia are typical of governments' efforts to tap these resources of human endeavour, while communities still hang on to traditional rural objectives of self-achievement.

In the more sophisticated First World, the Western world, after the passing of a century of industrial revolution and specialised education, many of these basic human skills have been lost. Modern society in the developed world now relies more and more on others for doing the most simple and menial tasks for survival. This reliance on others has, in many cases, left us with a society based on dependency. Whereas in such a sophisticated society we need social concern — particularly for the elderly, the infirm and the poor — this reliance culture has also taken away some basic human rights from ordinary, healthy, lively families.

I believe, even in the West, it is a human right to be able to build, add to and improve, and maintain the place in which we live.

The route to accepting this most basic premise is strewn with the garbage of so-called sophisticated specialist technical thinking. For example, what damage was caused by Le Corbusier's most irresponsible of statements when dealing with homes — that of providing 'machines for living'? He, like other well-meaning Modern Movement pioneers, thought that the technician could provide for ordinary working people from the cradle to the grave. The resultant dependency syndrome, although founded on very insecure foundations of logic, was actually welcomed by governments of both political persuasions; both Harold Wilson's and Harold Macmillan's governments of the Sixties wanted to build half a million houses a year. This building programme ruptured not only our building industry but also people's lives. Many families have spent the last two decades recovering from such misguidance.

There was no room in these great housing theories for the role of the individual. Machine-made products imported from Germany, France and Denmark were simply bolted together on site. Personalising each individual home was sacrificed for the mass-production process. Speed was of the essence; and compounding this already tragic direction taken by housing managers and the back-up agencies which supported them, was the need to digest whole tracts of otherwise reasonable older property. Much of this older property was the epitome of reasonable community life, although lacking in some areas as a result of wear and tear, and up-to-date technical innovation.

We now know, to our cost, with clear hindsight, that because a house failed to meet all the criteria laid down by the Public Health Inspectors, that alone should not have been the reason for the wholesale demolition and compulsory purchase clearance proposals which became so essential to provide the land for the redevelopment programmes of the Sixties and Seventies.

This book, then, **BRICK BY BRICK**, is welcomed in that it further strengthens the community architecture cause of allowing ordinary families a role in the provision of their own housing. This role has grown steadily to a point where the number of units now being produced by the self-help groups exceeds that being produced by the individual leaders of the house-building profession. More homes are being built by self-helpers than Barratt or Wimpey and the course is set fair for more and more participants in this blossoming movement.

But there are problems, and one of these, of course, is land. Self-help only succeeds when there is a reasonable base of affordable land. Another new problem is the availability of building materials at a time of unprecedented boom in the building economy, fuelled by demand from the private sector. This demand is equal almost to that channelled into house building by the public sector 20 years ago. Building materials are, increasingly, in short supply.

Self-helpers need to organise themselves in such a way that they are at the forefront of the demand for these materials and I would like to think that the self-build movement would also lead a campaign to ensure that local British building materials and locally-manufactured building products are made more and more available — not only to themselves for their self-help building, but also to the building industry as a whole.

It seems that so much that could be produced here in the UK is imported from outside our shoreline. Isn't it strange to buy slates from Spain when the Welsh hills are full of them? What is the logic of buying ceramic products from

Foreword

Europe when we once led the world in the production of such products? And the greatest irony of all, perhaps — why do we import Romanian cement?

The present demand for more and more building materials could go one of two ways — one, to awake the consciousness of those who could encourage home production of building materials. The other would be simply to endorse a steady flow of regular materials from abroad, further stultifying home based products. I hope it is the former.

The self-help movement must further encourage self-help in Britain's building products industry. I can say this because it is becoming a major force, economically as well as sociologically — two reasons why it will continue to succeed and help in the overall drive to provide decent housing for all in a modern society.

Self-help housing is good for the individual, the group, the community and the health of the nation — economically, sociologically and politically. People's self-assurance and self-attainment are its hallmarks.

RH
January 1989

1. Introduction

DAVID LAWSON, *property writer for* The Guardian, *assesses recent trends in the self-build movement from one-off individuals to organised groups. By listing some of the personal qualities self-builders have in common, he shows that it is possible for anyone to build their own home — provided they are as dedicated as his old friend Fred...*

Have you got what it takes?

A few years ago a neighbour of mine (let's call him Fred to save embarrassment) decided he needed a garage to protect his sparkling new Ford Cortina from the ravages of local kids, pigeons, rain — all the things invented to mess up status symbols. Having spent all his cash on the car, however, he decided he would have to build his own garage. Every spare minute for months he was outside measuring, marking, digging, humping cement and bricklaying. Part of the walls fell down at least twice and he rebuilt the roof three times, but eventually it was finished. Then he moved his bed in to the garage.

While Fred had been feeding his obsession, Freda was inside gradually exhausting her patience. I remember all this because she got the house after the divorce and he became a local celebrity by squatting in his beloved garage until the police heaved him out.

Fred symbolises the single-minded dedication of so many DIY builders I have met. They all seem to start tentatively, almost petrified by what they have taken on. But once into their stride, confidence bursts out as they realise that most domestic buildings can be mastered if you stick to the rules.

The last I heard of Fred, he was building a proper home somewhere on the south coast. He said he had to: he had no money left to buy one after Freda was finished. But I get the feeling he was irretrievably lost to the obsession anyway.

Douglas Graham's story on page 17 is a fine example of what can be achieved through such single-mindedness.

DAVID AINLEY, Commercial
Lending Manager, National
Provincial Building Society,
explains how the society can help
the self-builder in Chapter Seven. ▶

There is a limit to the capabilities of dedicated amateurs like Fred, however. Some skills usually have to be bought in for the complications of plastering, bricklaying, electrics and structural work. An architect or surveyor also has to persuade the local building inspector that the house will remain standing. But in 1987 more than 11,000 people managed to mix their dedication with others' skills successfully and qualify as true self-builders. That is a vast undercurrent of hidden activity considering that only a couple of the country's biggest house-building companies produced more homes that year.

Self-builders now have a bigger output than local authorities, which is partly a result of heavy spending cuts but also a reflection of the new interest being shown by housing associations, building societies and the local authorities themselves. Government figures for 1987 show that 9,500 self-builders reclaimed VAT spent on materials — all those who build for themselves and handle their own sub-contracting are eligible to do this, and must do so within six months of completing their house.

Murray Armor, one of the leading lights in this field, estimated that another 800 homes were completed by groups, and at least 1,000 by people whose VAT claims are hidden in business accounts.

Numbers are swelling all the time. The National & Provincial, which like other building societies is moving in strongly to back self-builders, predicts that £1.2 billion-worth of housing will be produced this way by 1990, almost three times the £450 million in 1987. Even if the soaring value of property is discounted, an expected output of 15,500 homes is still about double the contribution at the start of the 1980s.

Some enthusiasts see the wheel turning full circle back to traditions of self-help common before the agricultural and industrial revolutions. The rural poor often built their own cottages, while farmers and landowners would supervise the construction of a new house or mansion by craftsmen. It is easy to over-romanticise the connection between 16th century mud hovels and modern brick boxes, but there are parallels.

Self-help groups often resemble their rural ancestors because members have little chance of living in their own homes unless they build them themselves.

House prices — particularly in the south — have soared well beyond the means of many council tenants. Even renting has become a problem with the virtual moratorium on council building.

Yet the most common self-builder has chosen this path voluntarily. Individuals looking for a one-off home on their own plot of land may seem similar to the farmer or landowner of old but a few hundred years ago there was relatively little choice in the matter. Buyers had little chance to browse for their choice of dwelling until the Georgians invented speculative building in places such as Bath and London's West End. Even then, unless you had lots of money you put up with the designs they imposed and had to move to wherever the new

Introduction

homes were located. The same thing applied with the pattern-book builders who evolved through the 19th century into the volume developers of modern times.

Today's individual self-builders are generally looking for something different from the mass estates. They may want to stay in a particular place mass builders are not interested in; they may want a different sort of layout from the common throng; often they see the chance of snapping up a plot of land and producing a home much more cheaply than they could buy from the professionals.

Rising house prices have been a great influence on potential self-builders. Even if you have a nice home, the next step up the ladder becomes progressively further away as values soar. If, for example, you have a two-bedroom £50,000 flat and prices rise by ten per cent, friends will get fed up with hearing about your £5,000 "profit". But if you aim to move on to a £75,000 place with an extra bedroom, you find that it has gone up by £7,500, taking it even further out of reach.

Building your own home is one of the few legal ways of jumping the gap, as it can save anything from 25 per cent to 50 per cent of market price, depending on values in the area and the type of home. You save not just the developer's profit (which can average 20 per cent of the price) but all sorts of other costs the professionals bear, such as sales costs and overheads. The big saving which looms in most people's minds is labour, but this will depend on how dedicated a self-builder is to the task.

Because your new house will be your principle residence, the proceeds of the sale of your former home will not be liable for capital gains tax. While it would, in theory, be possible to reap a tax-free profit on the sale of successive new self-builds, the Inland Revenue will in all likelihood decide at some point that you are engaged in an 'adventure in the nature of trade' and you would become liable for income tax on all profits — retrospectively!

Some self-builders merely find the land, perhaps in the grounds of their existing home, and farm out all the work to professionals. Purists don't consider them self-builders at all, merely one-off developers. At the other extreme, people like Fred move into a caravan on the site and do much of the heavy work, leaving as little as possible to specialists.

There is a wide spectrum between these extremes, depending on how fit you are to carry out the drudgery and how much time you are willing to give up.

Most self-build groups expect members to sacrifice every weekend and holiday for up to 18 months — and impose penalties on slackers. Working alone can be soul-destroying, particularly through the winter, so strong motivation is essential to keep things ticking over. In fact it is probably as important as DIY skills or physical strength; there are examples of sweet old ladies building bungalows on hilltops where professionals would not tread, and many members of self-help groups have never been on a building site in their lives before.

The stories behind various group self-build schemes can be found on pages 33, 45 and 81.

This is why individual self-builders need an element of obsession — Murray Armor calls it the 'X factor' — because they have no-one to push them along. The most successful groups usually include some bricklayers and plumbers, but their most important secret is strong organisational backing, often from one of the firms set up to provide expertise in ordering equipment, planning schedules and generally keeping people moving.

They charge between five and ten per cent of the overall cost as a fee, but this extra cost can prove the difference between success and failure.

A classic example of group self-build is Surrey House in London's docklands, where Keith Julier of Essex Self-Build Advisory Service put together a deal with the development corporation to convert a former council block into owner-occupied flats. He sorted through long queues of potential members — all local authority tenants — to get the right mix. These come from all sorts of jobs and range in age from teens to couples in their 40s. Mr Julier, who has organised around 30 similar schemes since he got into the business 15 years ago, believes motivation and personality matter as much as building skills, as these people will have to work closely together for a long time.

The physical work is the easiest part of any self-build scheme, he says. The hardest is finding land, cutting red tape and sorting out organisation and finance. But he still needs to crack the whip to make sure members work closely to schedule. Perhaps the biggest pitfall with self-build is falling behind time, as interest on the initial finance can build up to a point where the cost of the eventual homes no longer appears cheap.

Self-builders — on site in London's docklands, — converting their former council block, Surrey House, into owner-occupied flats

Introduction

Local authority land is behind important developments in Tyne and Wear — the *centre of group self-build*. See page 33. ▶

The community schemes of Rosehaugh and others are looked at more closely in Chapter Eleven. ▶

As it is, the Surrey House group expected to end up with homes costing just over £55,000 each. Even with the slowdown in prices which engulfed London in late 1988, this was still around £30,000 below the market value at that time. But that was partly because of the way the London Docklands Development Corporation was keen to pass on the building rather than squeeze extra profit from a professional, as part of its policy of encouraging self-build groups. By the end of 1988 it had stimulated five schemes comprising 130 homes in the docklands.

These included the Isle of Dogs Self-Build Housing Association (most groups register as housing associations), put together by quantity surveyors Silk & Frazier to produce 34 houses at Maconachie's Wharf.

Members' skills included bricklaying, plumbing and woodworking, but others had jobs — from businessmen to taxi drivers. They each promised to put in a minimum of 1,730 hours to qualify for homes worth between £70,000 and £100,000. As in other groups, profiteers were discouraged by a rule that anyone who sold out in the first year could take only 20 per cent of the profit, with a sliding scale up to five years.

Local authorities have tried to follow the LDDC path by allocating spare land to both individual and group self-builders. But they face their own financial problems, which is where an unusual alliance between Prince Charles and Britain's biggest office developer comes in. Godfrey Bradman responded to a plea by the Prince for better inner city housing by inventing a financial formula which should allow sites to be released to self-build groups for renting or shared-ownership at a commercial return. The Prince has already inaugurated a 16-house scheme by Rosehaugh Self Build in the East End of London, where rents should fall within the housing benefit threshold at around £54 a week. Another 25 homes are being planned in Milton Keynes. The eventual aim is to provide an outlet for the low-paid, homeless, disabled and even prisoners coming out on parole.

But the real financial muscle is coming from building societies, which are taking self-builders to their hearts. The Halifax has backed Rosehaugh with £50 million and has 16 projects under way. Other societies like the Alliance, the Woolwich and National & Provincial are also going full steam. Individual self-builders often stumble here, however, as building societies are still not fully geared to single DIY development. But the N & P has marched to their aid with a revolutionary scheme for individuals to back up the £57 million it is pouring into group developments (including Surrey House).

In the past, anyone with modest means found it impossible to meet an expensive bank loan to build a new home alone. The alternative was selling an existing house to pay for a site and then moving the family into a caravan on the land for a year or so of purgatory while the place was taking shape.

The N & P has cut this knot by offering a 100 per cent mortgage up to

The Isle of Dogs self-build housing association on site in London's Docklands. John Morgan, of quantity surveyors Silk and Frazier, shakes on its success with Ron Gale, the group's on-site organiser.

£80,000 for the land and building costs, with payments suspended for a year to relieve money worries during the traumas of self-building. Controls on progress are tighter than those on any independent self-builder, with the society ensuring that work does not drag on so long that the rolled-up interest charges make the loan too big. But that will probably be a good thing for inexperienced builders, who often lack the discipline drummed into groups.

The individual will have an architect or surveyor to provide the costing and design — in fact the homes must have certification from someone with letters after their name to qualify both for mortgage support and local authority approval. But unless that professional takes a close personal interest, things can go badly astray.

Other building societies are likely to follow the N & P lead, so prospects for self-building look set to improve right across the spectrum, from groups with special needs through to individuals who want either to jump a few rungs in the price ladder or produce their own dream of a home.

I think Fred must be gnashing his teeth after jumping in too soon and ending up in a tiny caravan after losing his wife, his house and his beloved garage. But at least he still has his Cortina.

The first question to ask any self-builder is what made them do it in the first place? The second, is what kept them going? And the third, how did they ever finish?
Self-builders are a resilient bunch sharing similar characteristics. As with Douglas Graham of Keighley, it all comes down to determination, energy, and commitment...

The Beverley Hillbillies

It took many months of planning, saving, and sheer hard slog for Douglas and Gillian Graham to acquire their well-earned reputation as the *Beverley Hillbillies*.

The nickname has something to do with their brand new four-bedroomed detached house, the half acre of land on which it sits, and their three-month-old family car.

The comparison is a good one. As the middle child of a family of millworkers, Douglas identifies with his TV heroes, remembering what it was like to 'live in other folks' hand-downs and make do and mend'.

Now he too enjoys an unchanged lifestyle but in more comfortable surroundings — only, to his credit, he has done it all without striking oil.

It began when he married Gillian and moved from the mill's tied house to their own terrace house. Here was a chance to demonstrate his independence to the rest of the family. 'Everyone we knew rented their houses in those days. Buying was unheard of. They all called us mad fools, and I suppose we were because we were always broke.'

But 38-year-old Douglas is obviously one of those types whose determination to succeed forces him to take risks. In order to build his own home he had to sell everything he could. A past redundancy meant that the banks and building societies were reluctant to get involved.

'Could I get money out of any of them? Could I buggery. Talk about give you an umbrella for a shower and take it away for a storm — they were all the same. I couldn't get any of them to believe that when I said I was building my own house I meant it.'

And mean it he did. Undeterred by other people's scepticism, he suggested to Gillian that they should sell the house and the car so then at least they could buy a plot of land.

'She knows me when I'm serious, so she agreed. We moved into a tiny room of the father-in-law's flat. We had most of our furniture in with us. We literally had to climb into bed. I say bed, but it was actually an old mattress on the floor.'

He describes the plot he eventually bought as a 'farmer's back yard': 'The place was littered with rusty machinery and rabbit hutches, and even a World War II air raid shelter. But once it was cleared it was great to think that it was all ours.'

The start of the building work marked the beginning of a hand-to-mouth existence. They both worked full-time — Douglas as a contract worker with his own excavating equipment — and fed Gillian's father in return for their keep. Apart from the time spent on site, they stayed in during the evenings to avoid spending money. Both put all their spare cash into materials.

It is difficult to appreciate what motivates self-builders in the first place, but it's near impossible to understand what it is that keeps them going. With Douglas and Gillian, it was a mixture of pride and self-discipline that kept them on schedule.

'We set a finishing date and that was it,' says Douglas. 'I couldn't face the embarrassment of failing.'

That meant spending the best part of five months working a 14-hour day. He was working 25 miles away in Denby Dale at the time, leaving at 6.30 in the morning and not getting back until early evening, when he went straight to the site to put in a few more hours.

And he claims he didn't get tired. 'It was too much of an obsession. I couldn't have stopped even if I'd wanted to.'

The Grahams had become so fixed on the design of their house that had they not obtained full planning permission, they would have bought another site rather than modify the house to fit in. Similarly, when planning delays were preventing them from getting started, they took a chance, and got stuck in.

Along with spirit and strong will comes the confidence to have a go. Douglas's experience as a civil engineering contractor and a handful of mates in the building trade were sufficient to convince the Grahams they were up to the job.

He admits: 'I never thought about going wrong because I thought I could do it all.' This shows how enthusiasm can sometimes distort the truth, as Douglas was soon to discover that he still had things to learn. 'My main problem

Planning permission — or lack of it — should not be taken lightly. Deliberately flouting permission and 'taking chances' has cost many people dearly. ▶

was I wasn't very organised, and I also tended to worry about the money all the time.'

They sub-contracted most of the plumbing, electrical work, and second-fix joinery, and did everything else themselves. If Douglas was unsure about anything he simply asked around. 'Like the roof tiles. I'd never put them up before but really it's dead easy. They're designed to slot into each other. I soon worked out how to lay them by climbing on next door's roof.'

Gillian was doing her fair share of learning too. Although family commitments restricted the number of hours she could spare, when on site she insisted on helping out in every way she could. She mixed cement, carried bricks up the scaffolding, and drove the wagon. 'I did it partly to save money and partly because I wanted to prove to myself that I could do it,' she says.

Despite his worrying, Douglas reckons it was not his resourcefulness that helped as much as his tight hold of the family purse strings. 'All the time you have to think budget, budget, budget. It's easy in the early stages to keep adding a bit on here and there, but that's no good. I had to shop around all the time to get the best deal I could. I had to bargain with everyone. It's the only way.'

He cut out the middle-man by buying in all the materials and paying the sub-contractors only for their time. Despite the fact that these were his workmates he refused to pay any of them unless the work was done on time and up to standard.

'You've got to screw everybody down to the ground,' he warns. 'It sounds very mean, I know, but it's the only way to get the best deal. When you're building as you earn, every penny saved is a penny towards something else. I sometimes got materials at half what you'd expect to pay just by making a few phone calls and badgering a few folk.'

Hillbillies Douglas and Gillian Graham outside their new home 'Rivington'

With characteristic Yorkshire bluntness, Douglas Graham can hold his own. He recalls people's reactions when the Prestoplan timber frame first went up. 'Everyone round here called us *Little House on the Prairie* at first, which tickled me. I remember we had a load of gales just after it had gone up, and one night someone up this the street

...Every penny saved is a penny towards something else...

rang me up to say the hut had blown down. Well I thought he meant the house of course, so I rushed over like a maniac.' It was actually one of the farmer's old wooden huts which still hadn't been cleared from the site, and Douglas had a wasted journey.

Despite the teasing, the Grahams are thoroughly impressed with their timber-framed home. It was chosen initially because of its insulating qualities — 'you need to be warm up in these parts' — and with their recent quarterly bill for winter being less than half what they have been used to paying, it is living up to expectations.

That pleases the man who drives a hard bargain — as does the overwhelming interest of the finance houses.

'I can't get them off my back now,' says Douglas. 'They've seen I can do it, and now they can't lend me enough.'

Who knows, he may even need it. Determined to stay put for a good while, there are already mutterings of extensions, and then there's the rest of the half

acre to have a go at. Only if there is a next time...

'I'll get the money first and I bet you that from the first excavator bucket going down, I'll be done and dusted in 20 days. I'll set my stall out, and get a team of brickies on, and more subbies, and we'll work inside and out at the same time — no sweat. So how much then eh?'

But I'm not a betting person Mr Graham.

I'm not like you. I don't take risks.

JS

2. Choosing the best approach

'QUESTION: **Tell me, is yours an *individual self-build*, or a *group self-build*, or a *self-manage*, or a *group self-build-manage*, or a *sub-contract*, or a *part sub-contract*, or a *part group-part individual self-build-manage* or *what?* — And did you go it alone, or did you consult the consultants?**

ANSWER: **I'm not sure really. A bit of each I suppose.** '

Such will be the response from the majority of self-builders when you try to get to the bottom of exactly who did what on their house.

It's not because they don't want you to know — but more that, for most, the building work has been the result of month after month of collective hard graft leaving demarcation between people's trades or skills irrelevant.

So much so, that self-build has become the universal term for any newly built home not purchased from a commercial builder — whether or not building involved the owner getting dirty hands — and while would-be self-builders are recommended to leave further terminology well alone, it is essential to be aware of alternative options before starting. If only to help with background reading then, the simplest self-build glossary goes as follows:

- *Self-build* means you physically build your house yourself
- *Self-manage* or *sub-contract* means you organise others to build your house for you
- *Individual self-build* or *individual self-manage* means you build a house as a one-off
- *Group self-build* means you work collectively with other self-builders to produce a house for each member of the group, under the direction and guidance of professional management consultants
- *Group self-manage* means the same as group self-build but members organise and/or build without the assistance of consultants

And apart from allowing for different combinations of self-building and sub-contracting within each definition, this summarises the self-build movement in the smallest of nutshells....

Yet, deciding on the best approach is not always quite so simple. Experienced self-builders say that for every existing skill they were aware of, there was an equivalent one hidden away. Often reading or talking to an expert is sufficient to bring out unknown potential — so that before engaging costly sub-contractors or opting to go it alone you have to assess your anticipated, as well as existing, capabilities.

Add to this a realistic estimation of your available time and energy; the predictable unpredictables such as weather conditions, exhaustion and ill health; the awkward unanswerables like what happens when the enthusiasm runs out; and the necessary strategies for coping with the conflicting interests of family, friends, and work, and it doesn't make for easy decisions before getting started.

It's all right for self-builders to look back afterwards, make a note of what went wrong, and choose their next approach with twenty-twenty hindsight but none of this is of much use to the novice. Even the most practised and professional of sub-contractors are novices when building a complete home for the first time, and they face similar predicaments.

The secret is to have no secrets. Before making commitments to anything, or anyone, a thorough self-assessment is needed. The successful self-builder is the one who recognises personal strengths and weaknesses, predicting the problem areas and seeking the right advice at just the right time. Self-build requires honesty all round. If you have help then use it; if you don't, and you anticipate needing it, then get it. There is no point in struggling on indefinitely. Self-builders are survivors, not martyrs.

The package deal approach

What lies behind the success of so many self-built units these days — and accounts for the ever increasing accessibility of self-build — is the influence of a modern phenomenon known as the *package deal.*

Introduced by a handful of UK companies dealing in either timber-frame or traditional materials to attract non-tradesmen into self-build, the outcome of package deals has been to dispel the myth that to qualify for self-build you must already be ten acres and a pig on your way to self-sufficiency.

As the case studies indicate, the activity now has widespread appeal in every trade and profession.

The fact that the package approach neither undervalues the individual's input nor is deemed to be cheating, is reflected in its increasing popularity. Self-builders recognise the arrangement as a fully professional service enabling them to choose a well-designed home with the accommodation and facilities they need, at a price they can afford.

Companies differ slightly in the service offered, but the principle of selection,

Choosing the best approach

...The idea of selecting your ideal home from the pages of a brochure is not as far-fetched as it would seem...

A dream in the making — on the drawing board at Prestoplan Homes

modification, and consultation is much the same. And at a time when it's possible to shop by mail order, consult Teletext for prices and stockists, and book next year's foreign holiday — all without having left the house — the idea of selecting your ideal home from a design brochure isn't all that far fetched.

Neither is it programmed or predetermined. Companies like *Prestoplan Homes* (timber-frame kits) and *Design and Materials* (traditional materials) have their own architects and quantity surveyors whose specialism has become the ability to cater for client needs.

'Most of our customers know exactly what they want,' says Prestoplan's Managing Director Malcolm Hockless. 'Our designs are intended only as a starting point. The customer is encouraged to make changes, bring along the work of an outside architect, or commission one of our own design team to work on a new design from scratch.'

But the self-builder is buying far more than just a set of house plans. While these companies are generally only interested in helping serious would-be builders who have already obtained land, their representatives are able to step in at the early stages, advising on planning and building regulations, and design features appropriate to the site.

This is then presented as a preliminary study — for which only a nominal fee is charged — examining the feasibility of the client's specifications, along with detailed costings and a working schedule.

The consultants are responsible for the ordering and delivery of initial materials. It is assumed they will 'withdraw' at an agreed point, usually when either the timber frame is fully erected, or in the case of traditional materials, when the shell of the building is fully watertight.

In practice, they often stay around for longer. 'Building your own home is no small task,' says Bruce Macdonald, Manager of Design and Materials. 'Whether it's to put the customer in touch with experienced contractors, or simply visiting the site to see that everything is going to plan, we tend to be in the background. We cannot help but get involved. You see we're not just a drawing office with a few lorry loads of materials: we're a sophisticated builders' merchant offering an integrated, all-round service.'.

And the fee — a lump sum, usually with a deposit payable of around 25 per cent — is worked out accordingly. Package companies are at pains to point out that they charge the same unit costs for materials as ordinary builders' suppliers. In addition to the base cost of the kit, the customer pays a consultancy fee for the management, financial and architectural services received.

Details of package deal companies are given in Chapter Twelve.

Choosing the best approach
Case study

The fact that a recently widowed headmistress is able to prepare for her retirement by self-managing the building of her own home, is testimony to the attractions of the package deal approach — and an inspiration to any would-be self-builder...

This is the house that Marjorie built

One of the biggest nightmares about house-hunting is coming to terms with the fact that, no matter how much money you've got to spend, you will never get exactly what you want.

Either the garden will be too small, or the spare bedroom too dark, the expensive kitchen units not quite the right colour, or whatever — but at the end of the day it will be a matter of choosing your priorities and settling for the best compromise.

Unless, of course, like Marjorie Oldershaw-Smith, a headteacher from Derby, you decide to ignore convention and go your own way. She assures me that it's really not too difficult — at least not when you build as a package.

'It's because so much is done for you,' she enthused, 'you come up with the ideas and the firm balances them with common sense and all the necessary facts and figures.'

Marjorie had some very definite ideas about what sort of house she was looking for, even down to the finer details of where the sun should come in every morning. 'I wanted a bright kitchen at breakfast time and a sunny lounge to return to at night. I wanted low maintenance woodwork, and a warm, cosy atmosphere.'

But as *I want never gets*, Marjorie was quick to decide that the only answer was to forget the estate agents and actually build her new home.

This she did in less than 12 months with the aid of a package from *Prestoplan Homes*. The area manager first visited her in November, and she was unpacking her cardboard boxes by the following October.

During this time she continued to work full-time, took her annual holiday as normal, and dealt with the sale of her existing house. 'So you see it's all very easy!'

Marjorie's nonchalance about house-building has something to do with her background. Her father was an architect, and she has an obvious inherent sensitivity towards architecture and buildings.

Her family joined forces to build her first married home — the bungalow sold to purchase the kit for her new house, and — incidentally — in sight of the kitchen window of her timber-framed palace.

It was visiting friends in Ipswich that finally convinced her of the merits of timber-frame. 'It was a freezing cold winter's day and I can remember noticing how warm and draught-free their living room was.'

Then she was taken into their new extension. 'That was built out of ordinary building materials, and I'm not kidding you it was icy cold. The difference was quite remarkable.'

She returned with self-confidence, only to confront the anxieties of others. She had been recently widowed and many of her friends were worried that she would be taking on more than she could cope with. 'People thought it was too much for a lady of my age, and being female they assumed I would be taken for a ride.'

The Prestoplan service gave Marjorie the support she needed. The area manager escorted her to other self-build timber-framed homes, and took time to drive her around the neighbourhood looking at potential sites and architectural styles. Having found a plot of land in just the right spot, he was then able to advise her on the legalities involved.

Then it was time to crack on with the plans. 'This is a very awkward position with it being so narrow, and what with this and all my fussy requirements for the integral garage, coupled with the fact that I wanted a short driveway so I wouldn't have too far to dig the car out in winter, there was a lot of juggling around to do.'

Following Prestoplan's lead, Marjorie remained actively involved from start to finish. The company's consultants devised the working schedule, arranged for a builder, liaised with the gas and electricity authorities, and she dealt directly with the plumber and the electrician.

Much of the building took place over summer, and she spent most of her school holiday ferrying goods between suppliers and sub-contractors.

I wondered how the tradesmen responded to their female 'foreman' — 'Well usually it was fine but I must admit I had to be very particular and hold out until I was satisfied,' she said. 'I had to learn to be more assertive. I think I'd be better at it next time.'

Choosing the best approach
Case study

Mrs Oldershaw-Smith outside her new home in Derbyshire

JOHN MARSHALL

It all moved so much faster than Marjorie had envisaged. 'They told me these timber frames were quick, but not that quick!' She recalls the rapid transformation from foundations to frame — 'The kit arrived on a wet Wednesday afternoon, all packed up neatly onto the back of a lorry and by Sunday I had something resembling a house.'

Next came the cladding which Marjorie ordered in great abundance — 'I'm always paranoid about being cold so it was decided I should have insulation under the floor as well.'

And then came the preparations for the second fix. Here, the doors and window frames are fitted, along with the radiators and electrics. Despite initial complications brought about by the steeply angled gables of the dormer roof, Marjorie remains delighted with the house. Having had ample opportunity to discover any shortcomings in both the timber frame and the design, she is adamant that the layout is 'absolutely perfect', and is already appreciating total warmth at relatively little cost. 'I will never forget the feeling of dampness we had when we moved into the bungalow 30 years ago. In fact it made me quite ill.'

It is a false assumption to think that here is a dream made true for life — not so for a woman as ambitiously determined as Marjorie. Within months of moving in she was already planning her next home. 'Now that I've had a go for myself, it would be such a shame to waste all that experience.' **JS**

Group self-build

Those who, for whatever reason, find the prospect of working in isolation off-putting, have nothing to worry about, for there is always the option of joining a self-build group.

A group comprises any number of individuals who form an association and work together, on the same site, to build as many houses as there are members.

There are many advantages to building collectively in this way. Camaraderie and the sharing of skills apart, there are the financial and legal benefits. An association has the muscle for negotiating land purchase and obtaining loan funds — and there is much to be gained from the democratic, though formal, structure that group self-build inevitably imposes.

But then there are all the intangibles to consider: you must be confident of your ability to work as a team, sometimes sacrificing personal wishes for the benefit of others; you will have to be willing to comply with the rules and regulations necessary to ensure that members pull their weight and keep to schedule; you will need to be prepared for the possibility of fall-outs (remember that as these are your future neighbours, disagreements are best solved); and you must accept the fact that, no matter how wonderful your 'dream house', it will always resemble a dozen or so others.

Yet despite such potential minefields, the end result is that groups are now responsible for more than ten per cent of successful owner-built house starts each year.

This is thanks, almost entirely, to the foresight and business acumen of two or three commercial management consultants. Not unlike the package deal firms supplying house kits to individuals and groups, agencies such as *Homesmith Consultants* (formerly Wadsworth and Heath) have been quick to respond to, and in turn generate, a growth in demand.

Self-builders who build in groups demand guidance, some supervision, and professional support. To Homesmith Consultants — with a successful track record of more than 20 years, regional offices spread nationwide, and an annual target of 1,000 homes — group self-build has evolved as a finely tuned, well rehearsed formula.

The work of the consultants begins with finding a plot of land, which can be publicly or privately-owned, talking to planners to find out the sort of properties most likely to be approved for the site, and producing designs and costings.

At this stage the scheme is publicised locally — it is interesting that around 95 per cent of self-builders build within a three mile radius of their existing home — and a public exhibition is held for people to come along and ask questions.

Anyone interested in taking part in a scheme is asked to complete a straightforward application form giving details of financial status and any

The typical responsibilities of a management consultant are listed in full on page 30. ▸

Choosing the best approach

building experience. Within a couple of weeks of first announcing the scheme, applicants are shortlisted and invited to interview. Director of Homesmith Consultants, Bruce Heath, explains the thinking behind the selection procedure:

'The way we pick a group is to aim for a balance of tradesmen with non-tradesmen. While we have had groups entirely of non-tradesmen it is a struggle and can be costly because they end up buying the skills in.

'We work on the basis that a traditional two-storey house contains about 47 per cent unskilled labour — ideally, the rest is made up of specialists from each trade and experienced all-rounders.'

So the larger the group, the fewer specialists are needed. Bruce Heath estimates that groups of ten or fewer require virtually all skilled tradesmen, while groups of 20 are effective with only 12 experienced members, and groups of 30, with as few as 15.

But there's more to group self-build then teaching others to mix concrete. 'We are looking for commitment and the ability to get on well,' says Bruce Heath. 'Members have got to submerge their own requirements into the group. They have got to blend in and not be rebels.'

That is why so much emphasis is placed on the interview. Bruce Heath meets applicants and partners to discuss their accommodation needs. A wide range of property types can make for tricky match-making, although the company takes a pride in being able to award applicants their first choice.

While the design of each house is agreed in advance, its actual position on site isn't. Group members must wait until the first team meeting where lots are drawn to decide who will live where.

For once the group has been chosen, consultants begin to stand back. Discussion begins and democracy is introduced. Now is the time for the group's natural leaders to emerge. Members are encouraged to speak their minds and anything up to six or eight meetings are held before work even begins.

The order of completion moves logically from the edge of the site inward. Members elect one another for jobs such as group accountant, buyer and secretary. Outline rules, including the number of weekly hours to be put in and the amounts absentees will be 'fined', are decided by majority vote.

Because the consultants can be left to deal with the administrative headaches of planning applications, loan facilities, book keeping and VAT returns, it is possible for members to be out on site within six weeks of having first thought of building their own home. Equally reassuring is the knowledge that, under the watchful eye of the company's experienced site manager, and with personal commitment permitting, your new home will be ready within a promised magical period of time — usually 15 months.

Just as comforting are the financial arrangements. Apart from an initial down payment of a mere few hundred pounds, the cost of building materials and plant hire comes from association funds — a hefty loan secured by the consultants

What management consultants actually do...

- *Purchase the land and handle easements (eg. rights regarding adjoining properties), rights of way and so on.*
- *Arrange for mains services — sewerage, water, electricity — to be connected at the site.*
- *Advise on the organisation of the self-build group and take responsibility for all its legal affairs.*
- *Commission an architect to draw plans and deal with planning consents.*
- *Provide a detailed budget and work programme for the group.*
- *Negotiate finance for the scheme, arrange repayments and help individual members to obtain mortgages.*
- *Issue monies for building as and when required.*
- *Keep up to date with the group's accounts, prepare monthly statements listing costings, and handle all VAT returns on the group's behalf.*
- *Finalise the accounts by sorting out stamp duties, legal fees, mortgage transfer fees, interest charges, and so on.*
- *Advise on sub-contract labour and the hiring of machinery. Negotiate prices as necessary.*
- *Arrange for routine inspections by an independent surveyor to ensure that the necessary certificates are issued to satisfy mortgage requirements.*
- *Retain a contracts manager to be responsible for progress on site, and provide help and support.*
- *Inform the group of any increase in the price of materials, interest rates, and so on.*
- *Attend the regular meetings held between members, chairing and advising as appropriate.*
- *Aim for a smoothly run scheme offering technical advice, moral support, and professional opinion throughout.*

Choosing the best approach

and carefully staggered to keep interest rates to a minimum. This means that each member does not begin mortgage repayments until every house is complete, and every owner moved in. Each house is occupied as soon as it is ready, but on a licence-to-occupy basis with rent — equivalent to the eventual mortgage repayments — paid to the association.

The self-build horror stories of overdrafts and hurried house sales to raise the necessary cash to get started, not to mention the difficulties of living cramped together in some rickety caravan, no longer apply to group self-build. Members can delay the sale of their existing home until completion is imminent, enjoying the benefits of comfortable surroundings in the meantime.

Indeed, Bruce Heath believes it is certainties like these that soon convert would-be loners to the merits of teamwork. 'They come to us and we can tell them *where*, *when*, and *how much* in a matter of minutes. It is not a case of ifs and buts because all the information is there. We believe we are helping motivated individuals to get more for their money. Self-builders don't look to save money for its own sake. They still go for the biggest mortgage possible, but in the understanding that they will get twice as much house for it. The fact is, we give people what they want.'

And for the privilege, Homesmith Consultants charge about eight per cent of the aggregate value of the properties for their service. The price quoted for building a property is always inclusive of this fee, but does not allow for inflation. The company takes the view that as any inflationary increase in the cost of materials will be far outweighed by the corresponding rise in the real value of any self-built house, there is little point in trying to make predictions.

What Bruce Heath and colleagues do guarantee however, is that as long as building work remains on schedule, there is little room for error. 'Our figures tend to end up somewhere between five per cent under the quoted price to eight per cent over. We state that it can be done in the time we say, but we are not magicians. At the end of the day, the accuracy of our price depends on the hard work of the members.'

Right — *Local authority land in South Shields now being cleared for group self-build*

Inset — *Self-built homes in Tyne and Wear are gradually replacing run-down prefabs such as these*

Below — *Typical of the area's new look are these homes self-built by local people, many of them previous council tenants*

The surest way to learn about group self-build is to visit the very heart of it.
This is in the North-East of England where schemes by Homesmith Consultants are transforming sections of run-down housing estates into attractive residential areas...

Capital of group self-build

There are rumours in South Tyneside that when little old ladies are travelling on the buses, they have more important things to talk about than their private medical histories or the weather.

For, like everyone else in the area, they now have all those self-builders on their minds. Apparently, they swap stories about how long it takes to build a house and how much money can be saved. Often they compete to see how many folk they know who have built their own homes.

It is no exaggeration. Group self-build has taken off to such an extent in Geordieland that just about everyone knows someone who has taken part in a scheme.

So much is this so, that Homesmith Consultants' Area Manager, Mark Turnbull, has been forced to move his temporary office out of his dining room, open a second office in Scotland, and take on more staff to cope with the growing interest.

It began with six schemes — completed from the North-East office in three years. These became the catalyst for a further nine sites, and more than 300 properties in all. Success has bred on success, culminating in plans for ambitious self-build renovation projects and the Sunnyside scheme, near Gateshead, claimed to be the biggest ever self-build group, offering 90 new units.

Such progress has been the knock-on effect of South Tyneside's Labour Council's willingness to release local authority land specifically for self-build. Receptive to alternative ideas on urban renewal, and aware that large commercial builders have little interest in developing pockets of land amid council housing estates, the authority recognised the value of organised group self-build.

Mark Turnbull is convinced that the schemes have played a vital role in providing local people with a better quality of life: 'We can keep residents in their immediate home area and move them from rented prefabs into detached three and four bedroomed properties. There's no way they could afford to buy homes built to such high specifications from an ordinary builder. Which is why the "big boys" are rarely interested in the first place.'

The irony is that now the 'big boys' are proving to be the main providers of land for self-build. Contractors such as *Bellway* are busily selling off sections of their prospective sites so that visually, individual self-build schemes merge with the ubiquitous box-style development seen on any new housing estate.

But the contrast is marked. You don't have to be fond of new housing to appreciate the difference. Group self-build is mostly criticised for offering the same few designs, and yet compared with some of the uniform architecture seen on the open market, the choice is remarkable.

In South Tyneside, self-builders are living in anything from square single-storey units to elaborate mock-tudor 'mansions'. Within each site, there are external variations sufficient to interest the eye without standing out. House density is kept to below ten units per acre, as opposed to the usual dozen or more.

Nowhere are contrasts more remarkable than at those sites hidden among acres of pre-war council housing, run-down prefabs and open wasteland — small wonder that self-build is attracting so much attention.

At one exhibition advertising a scheme for 28 houses, Mark Turnbull spoke to 280 people, and received 128 applications. It concerned him that so many were being turned down. 'Quite honestly, we could fill our schemes on a Friday night by meeting people down at the local pub. We are now noticing the same folk applying scheme after scheme.' With predicted savings of 28-40 per cent on each house, who can blame them?

Mark Turnbull has no illusions about money being a prime motivator. A trained civil engineer, he was introduced to Homesmith Consultants as a self-builder on one of their earliest schemes. 'Being a self-builder certainly moved me right up the housing ladder. I got as far in 15 months as I would have got in 15 years through the usual buying and selling network. I take a pride in what I have achieved, and hope that other self-builders feel the same about what they have done.'

Feelings are very important to his personal style of management. Perhaps it is because he has been through the trauma of difficult working relations himself that he now takes a fairly philosophical view.

Choosing the best approach

Case study

...Compared with some of the uniform architecture available on the open market the choice is remarkable...

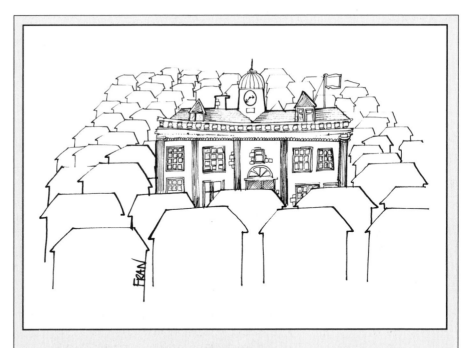

'Every group has its ups and downs. The disharmonious group now will not be the same as the disharmonious one in six months time. Let's face it, when 20 men get together, each with their own ideas and aspirations about building their dream home, then it's bound to get heavy.

'We're talking about 20 headstrong individuals with gumption, not 20 Mr Averages. Telling them they've got to start working as a democracy isn't easy. It will always create tension and conflict — especially when the disruptive individual in one person's eyes, is not the same one as in someone else's eyes. It's all highly subjective.'

The boss is not alone in having been a 'non-tradesman' applicant. Most of the North-East management team began on self-build schemes, leaving careers in engineering and surveying to join the staff full-time. This has obviously influenced their attitude towards mixed groups.

The Tyne and Wear schemes comprise a maximum of 65 per cent tradesmen. 'The non-tradesmen have so much to offer in terms of organisational skills, energy and enthusiasm. Yes we do look for strong groups, and the faster they are the better it is for us, but it is vital we give other professions a chance,' said Mark Turnbull.

In fact, the aim is to be fair all round. Where possible, and always when local authority land is involved, preference is given to those with obvious housing needs. Councils insist on vetting lists of applicants before places are

More up-market are the 35 mock-Tudor properties in the Hadrian Park scheme, North Tyneside

offered. They veto second-time self-builders, and are keen to eliminate potential speculators. Although Mark Turnbull appreciates their concern, he is reluctant to take on a charitable role. 'The council sees self-build as catering for the locals and resents those who sell up to make a quick buck. I accept this view, but this would mean imposing covenants on properties to restrict the movements of people and I don't see there is an argument for that. We're a business, not a public service.

'We look out for signs of speculative dealings at the selection stage because these builders tend to be apathetic and bad news for the group as a whole — but this is more out of practical common sense than a feeling of moral responsibility.'

Yet, like it or not, as long as Homesmith Consultants are able to rehouse residents on such a scale, improving the local economy and aesthetics in the process, self-build in Tyne and Wear will continue to make an impact. Albeit not as grand an influence as such advocates of enlightened Victorian paternalism as Rowntree and Salt, Homesmith Consultants are responsible for social engineering of a kind, and Mark Turnbull certainly makes it his business to be the one setting the precedents.

JS

3. Finding a site

MURRAY ARMOR — editor of *Self-builder* **magazine and author of various books, including** *Building Your Own Home* **— has been actively involved in the movement for more than 20 years. From his self-built home in Nottinghamshire he runs** *Ryton Books,* **and advises on all aspects of self-build. Here he suggests how to find, and purchase, a piece of suitable land...**

First things first

The actual business of buying the land on which to build your new home is easy, and is at the end of a long process which has involved working out what you can afford to buy, finding sites to look at in the right price bracket, knowing what to look for when you have found one, and understanding what has to be checked out to make sure that you can build the sort of house that you want within your budget.

First of all, if you are going to spend a huge sum of money on a building plot, and then spend an even larger sum on building a home on it, you have got to gen up on all aspects of self-building. You have made a good start by buying this book, but it must be the first stage in making yourself as much an expert on every aspect of building for yourself as you possibly can.

You should not commit yourself in any way to buy a piece of land until you have done all your homework. Only then will you be in a position to work out what you can afford to spend in total, and the proportion of this sum that can be used to buy the plot. This proportion will vary in different parts of the country, with the land cost being anything from a quarter of the total budget in the North of England and the West Country, to more than half in the South.

Sources of further information and contacts are listed in Chapter Twelve.

The balance of your money will be spent on the building work, and having got guide-line figures for the costs per square foot of the sort of home that you want, you will be able to work out how large it is going to be.

Complicated? Not really. Let us suppose that your total budget is £75,000, and that you live in a part of the country where the land usually costs a third of the total cost of a self-built home. This means that you must look for plots costing up to £25,000. You have discovered that typical self-builders' costs for the sort of home which you want to build in your area are about £26 per square foot, so you know you can build a house or bungalow of about 1,800 square feet. Careful study of books of plans has given you a clear idea of what accommodation you can expect in a building of this size and what it will look like.

Putting all this together, you can now look at plots in the right price bracket and make up your mind whether they are likely to suit the house that you want to build. Beware of trying to put too big a house on a small site, or a small house on a site bigger than you require, because you certainly want your new home to be the best possible investment. Not only do you have to be able to judge what you can hope to build, but you also have to be sure that it will be the sort of property that will sell easily whenever you decide to move on.

To find a selection of plots in the first place you have to realise that it is no use waiting for someone to come along who wants to sell you your dream building site: you have got to get out to find it and buy it yourself. How easily this is done depends on where you want to live.

In the South East and other parts of the country where property values are very high, it is extremely difficult to find any sort of land for sale, and plots are rarely advertised. Elsewhere things are easier, and you may find plots are advertised on a fairly regular basis in the local papers. Wherever you want to build, take heart from the fact that literally thousands of families will move into self-build homes this year. They all found land to build on in one way or another — and so can you.

Making a start

An obvious way to start is to call on all the estate agents to ask to be sent details of any individual plots which they are asked to handle. In high value areas these will usually be sold by auction or private tender, but elsewhere they will have a price tag like a house for sale. Do not be afraid of calling at the estate agents' offices regularly to enquire if they have anything new: on your umpteenth visit you may be told that details have just come in of a plot that may suit you and you will have chance to move quickly before anyone else does.

Another approach is to advertise in the local press. A small advert saying "Private purchaser requires building plot for own new home" may draw replies

Finding a site

from people who are nervous of selling to builders, or may even result in a phone call from a builder who wants to sell off a plot from his land bank but who does not want it to be public knowledge.

Local developers are often prepared to sell off one or two individual plots as soon as they have bought a site which they intend to develop, so releasing cash to pay for the roads and drains. This is becoming quite common, so consider sending a carefully worded letter to all the builders whose boards you see in your chosen areas.

If you already live near to where you hope to build, you can keep an eye open for unused pieces of land which seem to be obvious building plots, and make direct approaches to the owners. This can lead to some direct rebuffs, but a surprisingly large number of self-builders obtain land in this way. Personal contacts are obviously a great help and make sure that all your acquaintances know that you want to hear of any, and every, opportunity to find somewhere to build. Similarly, if you want to let it be known that you will give a couple of hundred quid to anyone who points you in the right direction, you will only be doing what all builders and developers do.

One route to finding the right opportunity is to call at the Town Hall and ask to see the Planning Applications List, which as a ratepayer you are entitled to study. This information is sometimes printed in the local papers where, among a mass of other entries, are listed the names of those who are seeking outline planning consent on a single plot. The applicant's name may be that of an agent, but it gives you a start.

An alternative approach is to get in touch with one of the local authorities which has special schemes to help self-builders, and which sells serviced building plots to those who want to build for their own occupation. These plots are often large, and in very good areas. The only way to find these helpful councils is a quarterly list called *Self-Build Opportunities*. Typically this lists about 70 self-build housing associations seeking members and 40 or 50 local authorities with either current or forthcoming schemes to sell plots to individuals, with details of whom to contact.

See Chapter Twelve for details. ▶

Eventually one of these different ways of finding a plot to consider will lead to you standing in the road looking at it, thinking about your budget, costs per square foot, and whether a house on it will be the right investment. If you decide that it is worth further consideration, then there is even more thinking to do.

At the very least, you are obviously going to consider all the factors which you would take into account if you were buying a home that was already built on the site: how near it is to work, schools, and shops, what the rates will be, whether it is in the sort of area that really suits your lifestyle, and so on. If all this checks out, then you can get down to the question of how easily you can build on it.

Remember that you can apply for outline planning permission on any site, providing you advise the owner you are doing so. ▸

Assessing a site

The first question is what sort of planning consent the plot carries, and whether this will enable you to build exactly the home that you have in mind. Watch out for any plot where there is no planning permission at all, even when assured by the vendor that outline planning consent will easily be obtained. In truth, you have about as much chance of this happening as you have of winning the pools. Virtually no-one with land that has even a remote possibility of obtaining planning consent will sell it without arranging for this themselves. Still, people do win the pools...

Next, you will have to consider the availability of services, including main drains, surface water drains, water, electricity, gas, and telephone wiring. Ideally these services will be available in the road, and all that you will have to do is to apply for, and pay for, the appropriate connections. This is rarely as simple as it sounds unless the land is being sold with 'all services available' as when you buy a plot on a local authority self-build development.

The best sort of drains are the surface water ones which take the rainwater from your roof. In the absence of these, it may be acceptable to build a soakaway instead, but do check beforehand. Foul drains take all the waste water from inside the house, and are usually connected to a sewer. Ideally, a sewer should be reasonably close to where you want to position the house, and down hill from it. If there is not one there, then you will need either a septic tank, a cess pool system, or a small domestic sewage pump. In recent years there have been new approaches to all of these alternatives which make sewerage problems less of a restriction when choosing a site.

It is unlikely that you will find that land has outline planning consent unless water and electricity services can be provided, but if they are not already available on the boundary it is essential to find out what the connection charges are going to be. Telephone services cannot be taken for granted — remember that since privatisation, connection charges can be very steep for more isolated homes.

Access is also important, particularly if the plot is on a through road. In this case the detailed planning approval will usually require provision to be made for a drive with a turning area which will enable a vehicle to turn round inside the boundary of your plot, which takes up considerable space. If the plot is on a cul-de-sac or a very minor road a simple drive which requires cars to back out onto the road will probably be acceptable. Besides the difference in cost, a drive with a turning area may take up so much of the frontage of a small plot that it will restrict the size of house or bungalow that can be built on it. The planners will also require that you arrange visibility splays at the entrance, so that the driver of a car pulling out onto the road can see clearly in both directions. Undeveloped plots on main roads are there because they fail to meet all these requirements.

Finding a site

Check list for finding and buying a site

BEFORE LOOKING

1. Establish budget. *(Made up from cash available, proceeds of selling existing home, mortgage available on present earnings and so on.)*

2. Consider what proportion of budget to be spent on land. *(Depends on where you intend to build.)*

3. Establish likely costs per square foot. *(Remember inflation.)*

4. Use all this to establish size and style of home. *(Remember the budget.)*

5. Get a clear mental picture of intended home. *(Books of plans will show range of styles available within definite price brackets.)*

6. Start looking at appropriate plots. *(Consider all angles — price, location, amenities, convenience, outlook and so on.)*

ASSESSING A SITE

1. Give thought to planning situation. *(Access, drainage, water, electricity and gas supplies, and telephone.)*

2. Examine site characteristics. *(Slope of land, possible foundation problems, covenants, easements, shared access arrangements, protected trees on the site and so on.)*

3. If no hiccups, then brief solicitor. *(Solicitor will contact the vendor's solicitor and start making searches.)*

GOING AHEAD

1. Negotiate a price. *(Solicitor will advise.)*

2. Retain an architect. *(He or she will make enquiries at the planning office to check plans are generally acceptable for the site. As a prospective purchaser, application for outline planning permission will be made.)*

3. Apply for services. *(Water, electricity, and gas.)*

4. Check if there are expected foundation difficulties. *(Architect often does this by consulting local authority building surveyors.)*

5. Arrange mortgage if needed.

6. Sign the contract to buy the land. *(Solicitor will advise.)*

7. Take out self-builder's insurances. *(Do this long before building work starts as cover against untoward happenings on the site.)*

Insurance details for self-builders are given in Chapter Twelve.

Sloping sites present other problems, to which there may be cheap and attractive solutions, or which may take development costs well beyond your budget. Level sites near a river may be liable to flood, and the water authority may insist that floor levels should be above the level of the highest flood ever recorded, even if this was in 1830. The cost of this may explain why the plot has never been built on before, but perhaps changing values make it cost-effective to do so now.

Think also of the possibility of foundation problems. Again, modern building techniques enable new homes to be built on plots which have remained undeveloped because they are on 'bad land'. The cost of building special foundations on sites with such problems is often less than anticipated. A gap in a village street where nothing has been built because it was once the village duck pond may now be capable of being developed using short bored piles for the foundations at a surprisingly reasonable cost. If this can be reflected in the price of the land, or in the value of the finished home, then it can present a special opportunity to build a dream home.

All of this may seem very complicated and worrying, but your job is not to deal with these technical problems yourself, but to know what has to be given consideration. By the time you have read all the books, met other self-builders, and sent for brochures from all the firms offering services to those building on their own land, you will have a clearer picture of it all, and will know what questions to ask when a possible site comes up. Remember, you will engage an architect or designer to deal with the problems when you have bought the land: your concern is to know what you must look for when you are deciding whether or not to buy.

Negotiating a price

Once you do decide to go ahead everything starts at the solicitor's. The procedure is not dissimilar to a house purchase. The professional you engage will advise on how to make an offer and examine the title before you are fully committed.

Bear in mind that plots bought at auction are yours once the hammer has fallen, and there is no going back. In these instances, you must consult your solicitor beforehand. Alternatively, land bought through an estate agent will usually require a deposit. This is acceptable, provided the words *subject to contract* are evident, and the deposit is refundable if you do not proceed.

As with all house purchases, the process of signing subject to contract, followed by legal searches and a draft contract still applies. This always takes time — rarely less than a month — during which you will be in regular contact with the solicitor.

And in the meantime there is more to do than sit back and wait. You will

Finding a site

have to find an architect or design firm to prepare a site plan and drawings and handle the ins and outs of the planning application. You will be learning that owning a piece of land involves more than paying for it and moving on site. It is as difficult and as exciting as learning a new language and a new set of rules.

Members of the Irthlingborough self-build housing association pause for the camera in front of their future homes

David Hobbs applies the finishing touches to his new home

Self-builders near Northampton soon found themselves on a slippery slope to nowhere as they struggled to dig out their plot. It was an obstacle calling for professional advice, specialist equipment, and one-off design work. Their efforts stand as firm evidence that, with care, even the most problematic sites can be built upon...

A bargain at half the price

It's funny the things you discover when you start to build for yourself — like a load of mediaeval masonry buried underneath the ground. That was what the Irthlingborough Self-Build Association members unearthed when they started building six large four-bedroomed homes from traditional brick and block back in 1987.

The masonry was thought to be the remains of a conduit built centuries before — not surprising as the site disclosed a number of natural underground springs which in some places broke through the surface. As well as being rather wet, the area was also sloping — two factors which would determine how the house was designed and built.

Situated on a small corner of a larger plot where a well-known firm was building executive homes, the site was chosen by management consultants *Withers and Company* of Northampton and then bought on the open market by the Irthlingborough members. Before fixing a price with the vendor, Withers did a site test and found that although the ground looked relatively dry on top, underneath it had, said managing director, Andrew Withers 'the consistency of porridge'.

Withers engaged a structural engineering company to carry out a full bore test to take samples and find out how far down the builders would have to go before hitting solid ground. It revealed blue clay four and a half metres below the surface. Overlying this was an underground stream and, above that, sandstone.

See Chapter Twelve for details. ▶

The stream was probably the combination of natural artesian springs and water from the mediaeval drainage system. The site had to be piled for ring beam foundations to provide a firm base on which to build. This also allowed the water to continue its course in order to prevent a build-up of pressure. Piling contractor Roger Bullivant gave Withers a quote to do the work and the vendor deducted the amount from the final asking price.

Irthlingborough members helped in the positioning and marking out of the piles and one, a JCB driver, later pulled out the trenches for the ring beams which were part-excavated and part-shuttered. Members also helped to carry materials for the steel reinforcing cage which was fixed in place by professionals. Concrete was then poured over the steel and vibrated into position. All of this work was supervised by the structural engineering company which produced a certificate to say that everything had been carried out correctly.

The foundations were scheduled for completion at Christmas and everyone worked flat out to ensure this happened — including Andrew Withers who was still up to his waist in water on Christmas Eve helping with shuttering work.

Fortunately the slope aided drainage. Members, working with a ground-work contractor, laid a series of land drains which collected water from the high-level ground at the rear of the buildings and diverted it around and between the houses down to an existing open water course nearby.

The nature of any site will restrict the number of design options. At Irthlingborough all the association members agreed — on advice from architect Trevor Jolley who handles all the Withers schemes — to go with the same basic layout. He explains:

'It was much more viable to do it this way because of the nature of the foundations. All the piling and ring beams had to to be specially designed by an engineer and then checked by the council. If all the houses had been different that process would have to be carried out for each separately.'

The houses are built side-by-side on a split level with a garage on the lower half and most of the living accommodation on the upper. Although the basic design is the same, each has been given a separate character by using a variety of bricks, tiles, roof pitches and gables. Window and door fixtures and decorative leaded lights add further individual touches.

The Irthlingborough scheme was completed in just 13 months — one month behind schedule, but not bad considering the tricky start. That the initial problems were overcome so quickly and so successfully was due, says Trevor Jolley, to the fact that the association took professional advice right from the start:

'Self-builders aren't always experienced enough to know all the technicalities involved. It's essential to use specialists who can do things for them.'

BA

4. Overcoming the obstacles

DAVID SNELL — Regional Manager with self-build package company Design and Materials *— has been in the house business since he became an estate agent in 1963. He was building houses for other people when self-build was in its infancy, and built his own in 1971. A recognised expert in planning procedures, he explains the ins and outs of making an application...*

Applying for planning permission

Anyone wanting to build their own home must be familiar with the basic approvals needed on their dwelling. While it is the architect's job to deal with these, the procedures are so fundamental to the legalities and finance behind any self-build project, that self-builders can only benefit from a clearer understanding of what is involved.

The normal process of planning approval is to apply for ***outline planning permission*** and if this is successful to apply for ***detailed planning permission***, or ***approval of reserved matters*** as it is more properly called.

Outline planning permission establishes whether or not, in principle, a piece of land may be built on and what class of development will be permitted.

Approval of reserved matters deals with the details such as siting and design of the property, together with any other matters which were 'reserved' as conditions in the original outline consent.

In some cases where the principle of whether or not the land is suitable for building is not contentious, the two stages of the application can be rolled in to one full application.

If it is felt that the principle of whether or not the land is suitable for building is what has to be established, then it is better to make a simple outline application. This can often be done by the private individual simply filling in the form provided by the local authority and sending this in together with copies of the site plan and relevant fees — all of which is detailed in explanatory notes supplied by the local authority.

This application can of course be accompanied by a letter setting out the particular case, although it must be understood that planning consent attaches to the land and not to the individual. Therefore, in strict terms — although there are notable exceptions such as certain agricultural dwellings and workshops — the needs of a particular individual are not relevant.

To leave matters there can often result in a refusal but it is possible to raise the profile of an application by lobbying the local councillor and members of the planning committee. There is nothing wrong in this — at certain times your local councillor will ask for your support in the form of a cross on a ballot paper, so you are quite entitled to seek his/her support in this connection — so long as you don't indulge in bribery!

The best way of going about this is to prepare a written submission setting out the reasons which you feel make your plot suitable for development and to visit your local councillor by appointment shortly after the application has been lodged. Find out who your local councillor is, if you don't already know, by ringing the local council headquarters (your planning authority will normally be the district council). Ask for the names and addresses of the members of the planning committee and if your councillor feels it would be appropriate to visit certain members or ask them to visit you on site.

Two weeks before the application is due to go to committee, arrange for copies of your written submission to be made available to committee members. Any earlier than this and the contents will be forgotten — any later will mean that they would not have time to check up on various facts and/or visit the site.

Of course nothing can guarantee success in a planning application because although we are dealing with law it is nevertheless interpreted by people with their own opinions and prejudices. But by raising the profile of an outline application in this way you can ensure that it is considered fully and is not simply refused on the nod by a narrow cross-section of opinion expressed in an officer's report and recommendation to the committee.

It is of course the outline approval, even if it is implicit in a full approval, which confers the value on a piece of land by having got over the first hurdle. The next one, approval of reserved matters, has also to be overcome.

In general, this part of the application is best handled by a professional because at this stage the knowledge of design types and requirements of the local authority is important. Since the local government reorganisation of 1974 most local authorities have attempted in various degrees to stamp a regional

vernacular on property designs and in particular the use of external materials. While there are areas where it would appear that anything goes, in general, planning applications should seek to conform to local idioms.

In some cases, property — either because it is relatively isolated, or because of its sheer size — can be said to become an architectural unit in its own right, and in other cases it would seem that properties have been approved because of their adventurous or innovative design.

It is also possible to detect fashions and fads in design but probably it is better to avoid these. An example which we can all recognise is the 1960s bungalow built of brick or render with low pitch roof which now looks so incongruous in many of our villages. These can easily be dated and it could of course be argued that the fashion today for mock-Tudor homes could in 20 years time fall into the same category.

It is sometimes possible to come up against a situation in which the planning officers seem to support the application but the committee turns it down. Sometimes there is good reason for this and it is of course possible for officers to be out of step with local opinion as reflected by their committee.

In other cases it can be put down to the question of local politics and it is almost as if the local people are in some way happy to be overridden by the 'chap in London' and able to 'wash their hands' of a locally contentious issue. Conversely, applications recommended for refusal may be passed by the committee. Appeals should not, however, be entered into lightly — most of them fail and the reasons for refusal are upheld or even magnified by the inspector, so professional advice should be sought before proceeding in this direction.

What many people do not realise, however, is that it is possible to appeal against conditions in an approval without negating the approval itself. But the only criteria for such an appeal are on the grounds of the conditions being either unreasonable or unlawful. Again, professional advice should be sought before proceeding.

Development outside town or village boundaries is normally strenuously resisted and if you know of an example of development in the countryside then it is probable that this has been granted on an agricultural basis. Most county Structure Plans allow for development in rural areas so long as it can be proved that it is necessary for the proper and viable running of agriculture, and it is incumbent upon an applicant in these cases to prove the viability and properness of an application. This is usually assessed independently by a body such as the Ministry of Agriculture, Fisheries and Food. Such a consent, if granted, would normally limit the occupation of the dwelling to a person wholly or mainly engaged in agriculture or last engaged in agriculture, or the widow or widower of such a person.

In cases where the viability of the farm unit or enterprise is not in question, it is often advisable to go for a full application which combines the outline and detailed stages and by doing so the application is argued at the higher plane of 'what will be there and what will it look like?' rather than 'should it be there at all?'.

When dealing with your architect or other representative, remember that although they understand and sympathise with your emotions in this very important aspect of your life it is necessary for them to remain emotionally detached from the application and to argue in a calm and reasonable manner. While the applicant may feel that a particular officer or authority has a grudge against him, the architect or representative will probably have dealt with the officer before and must bear in mind that he will have to do so again on behalf of other clients for whom he must still do his best. So do not be surprised if your representative does not share your enthusiasm for 'bopping the officer on the nose'. Remember too that the officer is also doing his job within the environment and climate of opinion in his authority and is in no way vindictive towards any applicant. As a member of the public you have free access to planning officers and, invariably, if you ask for advice you will get it. They have a vested interest in building development and like to influence it by advice as well as control. Your application will be dealt with on its merits. The officer must approve what is acceptable — not what he thinks is best.

Conservation area, national park, area of outstanding natural beauty — these are terms calculated to strike fear into the heart of any self-builder. But as Stan Abbott — editor of National Parks Today — *writes, not all national park red tape imposes unreasonable restrictions...*

An English retreat

It is a misconception that there is any substantial difference in the way planning law is applied in any area of the country. What is true is that, in general terms, planning regulations in rural Britain as a whole are pretty tough.

At the outline application stage, planners apply the rule that there should be no new development in open countryside, outside existing village limits.

At the detailed stage, planners will stipulate that new developments should be in keeping with the prevailing architectural style in the area.

This applies equally to cities, towns and villages. In the case of national parks — which have been designated to conserve the special 'built environment' as well as their natural beauty — the application of these rules means that builders will generally be required to use traditional materials.

While this may mean that a house will be more expensive to build than its city counterpart, this will nonetheless be reflected in its eventual market value. And no self-respecting self-builder should want to create a red brick bungalow in a row of stone cottages any way.

Take the case of Fred Heyworth, who decided to build his own home at Coniston in the Lake District National Park.

Fred engaged self-build package company *Design and Materials* to turn his sketch plan into a detailed design that would be appropriate to the prominent site, with its commanding view across Coniston Water.

D and M's architects improved Fred's concept, creating a two-bedroom bungalow with garage and workshop below one end, and a mezzanine entrance porch. They liaised with officers at the Lake District Special Planning Board and the design was approved with a minor amendment to the location of the access drive and the stipulation that traditional Westmorland blue slates be used on the roof. Anticipating this, Fred and the architects had already opted for a simple roof profile that would lend itself to using natural slate rather than factory-cast tiles.

The national park authority also stipulated that the house should have a white roughcast finish, with the render 'mixed in the traditional manner and thrown on'. This meant the house would be in keeping with one of two styles prevalent in the village and was good news for Fred as the other local style involves a far more expensive stone finish.

Fred's self-build project was the result of a ten-year post running a technical school in Oman.

His overseas earnings enabled him to have a house built at Windermere as an English retreat during his three-month summer breaks. He watched the builders at work and thought: 'I can do this myself.'

The site at Coniston cost him £20,000 in 1986 and comprised two adjacent plots which had been on the market for some time because commercial builders had been deterred by the tricky access up a narrow steep hill.

By the time he returned for good from the Middle East in 1987, planning permission had been sorted out and — with his hard-earned savings behind him — he was ready to begin a two-year labour of love.

'I have worked a normal working week without pushing myself,' said bachelor Fred, 56, as he tackled the electrical wiring on a spring-like day in January 1989.

Fred chose D and M after reading about the company in a magazine and comparing it with reports on other companies. 'I didn't want to have a timber frame because, for one thing, you can't put the frame up single-handed — by choosing a "traditional" system I can do all the building work myself,' said Fred.

'I certainly haven't been disappointed — they have been very good and everything has come on time.'

The beauty of the package for Fred was not only a significant saving compared with what he would have paid for his materials from the local builders' merchant, but he also avoided the pitfalls of trying to do his own quantity surveying — an important consideration when all materials had to be off-loaded at a nearby car park and taken the last few hundred yards by dumper truck.

'D and M took a lot of the sweat out of it because I was sure that the materials that came would be right and things like the windows would fit together.'

The local authority building inspector soon became a regular visitor and — while he enjoyed a reputation as a stickler for the rules — Fred found him co-operative and helpful.

One year into the project and Fred's house was the proud owner of a roof

Overcoming the obstacles
Case study

Fred Heyworth at his new home above Coniston. The external walls will be rendered with roughcast to match the chimney.

in traditional slates salvaged at a cost of some £3,000 from a building in County Durham. 'It took me ages to do the roof, because the slates have to be laid in diminishing courses, starting at around 36 inches at the bottom and reducing to nine inches at the ridge,' said Fred.

He learnt all he knew from talking with local builders and mugging up from books. By January 1989, Fred had spent about £30,000 on materials, including £16,000 for the shell, and expected to spend another £10,000 on fitting out before moving in in the summer.

The cost of the site brings the price of Fred's house up to around £60,000, plus two years' labour. A conservative estimate of its market value would be around £100,000.

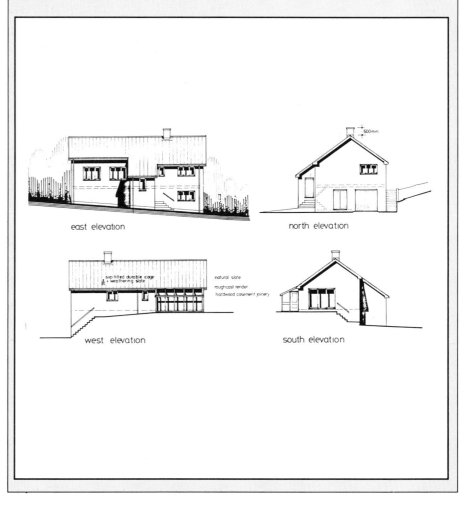

east elevation

north elevation

west elevation

south elevation

natural slate
roughcast render
hardwood casement joinery

The architect's elevations of Fred Heyworth's Lakeland bungalow show clever use of the uneven site to create an integral garage and workshop and mezzanine porch.

The clean roof design is pitched at 35° — rather steeper than on most modern houses, but in line with local planning preferences.

5. Sticking to the rules

Before joining the self-build package company Design and Materials, *first as Manager of a subsidiary company and then as a Regional Manager, TIM WOODS worked for eight years as a building control officer. It is this experience, plus his training as an architect, that make him the ideal candidate to answer questions on building regulations...*

What are building regulations?

Building controls vary in form and scope in different countries, some being based on a sort of insurance against building defects, while others, such as in Great Britain, seek to prevent or minimise the occurrence of defects through active enforcement of controls.

The building regulations under which we operate in this country evolved out of the very first Public Health Act of 1875, which allowed statutory control of building operations insofar as public health and safety would be affected. The scope of building regulations remained limited by definitions contained in that Act and succeeding 1936 and 1961 Acts until the Health and Safety at Work Act of 1984.

Today's regulations, together with associated legislation, codes of practice and other standards, set down requirements for ensuring that building work is structurally sound, properly protected against the risks of fire, is proof against the weather and moisture from the ground, constructed to minimum standards of thermal and sound insulation, and is satisfactorily drained.

Is all building work subject to the building regulations?

Virtually all building operations are subject to building regulations, the notable exceptions among residential premises being small detached buildings such as private garages, sheds, greenhouses, etc. which fulfil certain simple criteria as to floor area and distance from boundaries. Some very minor extensions to dwellings are also exempted, such as some conservatories, porches and car ports. (These should not be confused with 'permitted development', which is a term for certain extensions which do not require **planning consent**.)

Does everyone building a house have to comply with building regulations?

Strictly speaking, they do not, although of course everyone will be subject to some sort of control. Since November 1985 legislation has allowed a developer either to:

● Submit a **full plans** application and be bound by the requirements of the building regulations both at plan stage and during construction work on site.

● Give the local authority a **Building Notice** which does not need to be accompanied by plans of the proposals. The local authority will probably request information, but it will not be required to pass or reject details of the proposal.

In the latter case, the protection of having had your plans passed is not available. You must still ensure that the work complies with the regulations, and the building control officer may require work to be altered if it does not.

The principal benefit of this procedure is that you can start work without having to provide plans (assuming, of course, that you have other appropriate consents such as planning permission).

The onus for ensuring compliance with regulations falls on your own shoulders, and the inherent risks make this an ill-advised course for those building their own house.

A third option is also available, of bypassing the local authority controls procedure and engaging an independent **Approved Inspector** to be responsible for supervising the work. As no approved inspectors other than those of the National House Building Council (Building Control Services) have yet been appointed by the Secretary of State, this is rarely adopted other than by developers who will seek **type approvals** for a house design, and simply repeat it without having to keep having it appraised.

At this time, by far the greater number of individuals building their own houses stay with the time-honoured system of applying for building regulations approval, and having local authority building control inspections of work on site.

This probably has a great deal to do with the express need of the self-builder to have complete and authenticated documentation and approvals, so that the subsequent potential resale of the property is not prejudiced.

Sticking to the rules

Do the building regulations make any differentiation between self-builders and say, estate developers?

There are no concessions, and minimum standards are laid down for all to observe. In practice, however, the self-builder tends to exceed minimum standards (for example, putting more loft insulation in); whereas the speculative builder seeks to maximise his profit by satisfying minimum criteria only — unless, of course, he is aiming more 'up-market'. It is fair to say that the specification of self-built houses is generally superior and therefore the resale prospects are usually enhanced.

An important observation to make at this stage is that the local authority building control section is a fount of knowledge for the self-builder, and once the building control officer is satisfied as to your decent intentions, he can be an invaluable source of help and guidance. He can also make a formidable opponent for those who would cut corners!

Does the local authority have any real say in matters once the plans have been approved?

You are obliged by the regulations to ensure that work on site is in compliance, and there are stages at which you have a statutory duty to notify the building control section to enable inspectors to come and check the work for compliance.

You may, and almost everyone does, vary from the approved plans, but these departures or variations must first be agreed with the building control officer and the planning officer.

For work which does not comply with building regulations the council may take formal proceedings against you in the magistrates' court, and these may result in prosecution and fines. The building control officer is empowered to issue notices in certain circumstances, requiring work to be opened up for inspection (such as foundations backfilled before the inspector has seen them, and within the prescribed period of notice), or to be altered or taken down where shown to be in contravention.

Can building control procedures affect the progress of the project?

As with all bureaucratic processes, delays can occur, but in practice building regulation approvals are generally more quickly obtained than planning consents.

The statutory period within which the local authority must determine a building regulations application is five weeks from the date of deposit, unless agreed mutually in writing, which can extend the period to a maximum two months. As for work on site, the building control officer is not literally empowered to stop the work, even when there are defects, but one would be ill-advised to continue were this to be the case, without agreeing appropriate measures to avoid problems later.

Do building regulations approvals have a limited life?

Building regulation approval lasts for three years from the date of the Approval Notice. This simply means that work must be commenced within that time. There is no limitation on the time taken to build. It is generally not too complicated to renew an expired consent, provided that the legislation does not change radically in the interim period.

Are there appeals procedures against building regulation rejection, as there are for planning?

Yes, there are but they are of a very different nature to a planning appeal. You can appeal to a magistrates' court to challenge the 'reasonableness' of a refusal, but this procedure is practically never used. The reason for this is simply that, unlike planning permission, which is discretionary, building regulations approval cannot be denied providing the submitted plans show compliance. Therefore, rejected plans, once amended to show compliance, have ultimately to be approved.

What happens when building work starts?

You or your builder will give notice to the building control office when you start work, and at certain stages of construction.

Usually, building regulations approvals for plans are issued together with a series of inspection notices (often referred to in the trade as 'tickets') which are sent in to the council to advise that inspection of a certain stage is required. Each stage has a particular period of notice which has to be observed before proceeding to the next stage of work.

The building control officer will call at the site in response to the notice (some, but not all, authorities accept telephone notification) and after the first inspection an invoice will be sent to you by the council to cover the fee for all inspections to be made.

It can not be overemphasised for the self-builder that if you or your builder has a problem with any aspect of the regulated work, you should call the building control officer rather than pressing on regardless. Remember he has powers to require work to be opened up for inspection if covered over, or to be taken down if in contravention.

6. Choosing the best design

When it comes to design KENNETH CLAXTON is a name often associated with technical innovation. Before founding his architectural practice in 1976, he ran the technical section of the Royal Institute of British Architects. He has experimented with steel housing, and built his first house in 1970. His practice designs, funds, and manages group self-build schemes...

Designing your own home is a two-way process. It is based on a series of compromises between the dream and the reality: what the builder wants and what the limitations of the site and bank account will allow.

A basic component in this equation is the designer-builder relationship. And it is helped greatly if both parties are aware of what motivates the other. Self-builders have their own reasons for embarking upon building. Some have a desire to build their own nest, some want to get their foot on the property ladder and others do it solely as an investment.

It isn't up to the designer to question these reasons. Nor is it up to the self-builder to dispute a designer's judgment on what is and isn't possible.

Some architects assume the builder will construct what the designer has laid down on paper. But in self-build the client and builder are often the same — particularly when members of a group are drawn from the building trades. It's a strange situation for an architect when he has to criticise the workmanship of his clients in their own self-interest.

From the start it is up to the self-builder to be absolutely clear about what he or she wants. The designer must then fulfil these expectations while trying to make the building process short, easy and worthwhile for the client. The design process can then get off to a smooth start.

The first and most essential factor governing the basic design of any house will be the site. Location, type of soil and slope of ground will govern the style of house, its construction and the foundations on which it is built. For example, local planning restrictions won't allow you to build a Tyrolean chalet in the middle of the Yorkshire Dales; a sloping site will dictate a split level design; mushy soil will (probably) necessitate piled foundations.

Already, the number of options has decreased. The self-builder then must decide on the basic type of design. Reference to standard plan types can help a great deal here — most design practices will have a selection of past schemes to study.

However, if any one phrase can sum up my advice on how to go about designing a house it would be 'keep it simple'. When I built my own home back in 1970, I proved that construction could be simplified to the level of incompetence found in an amateur builder like myself. Of course the extent to which this applies will vary according to the nature of the project. Group self-build schemes will probably incorporate a wider range of skills than the individual possesses and this will allow a greater degree of sophistication.

The structure should be as simple as possible — refinements such as gable projections increase unit costs. A basic rectangular shape with two end gables is the most economic solution. Construction should omit complicated skills, particularly wet trades and those which are craft-orientated. Simplicity in ordering by using standard product sizes reduces waste and helps rather than hinders when you start setting-out.

An example of a first-timer's simple structure is this farm worker's bungalow in Wiltshire — built from traditional materials supplied by Design and Materials

Choosing the best design

...It is important for the designer to innovate in order to free self-build from its dependence on traditional building skills...

Because of their practical simplicity, self-build schemes rarely encounter problems when presented to planning authorities. But two points are worth bearing in mind. First, in cases where housing needs can be proven, some planning authorities tend to be sympathetic to self-build schemes on land which otherwise wouldn't be released for residential development. In such circumstances it is usual to tie the scheme by various legal agreements to first-time purchasers, or to adopt a form of tenure, such as shared equity, which controls the low-cost nature of the scheme.

The second point relates to the anti-social element in self-build. An awful lot of building work takes place during weekends and evenings which can cause problems with neighbours. On the whole, however, I have found that there is a considerable amount of public support for self-builders.

In some group schemes, members may not be able to afford to complete the house all at once. But it's worth remembering that a house can be designed to be finished to a habitable standard and the remainder completed when resources become available.

If these factors are taken into account, the basic structure of the house can be designed sensibly in order to be cost-effective yet at the same time versatile enough to allow a high degree of individuality.

Simplicity of the basic structure is important. Not only does it provide continuity and the initial speed of construction essential to sustain the early enthusiasm inherent in most self builders, it also allows a basic framework upon which the individual can later stamp his or her own personality.

Many schemes I've been involved in ended up as a competition between members to see who could provide the best fireplace surround, the best archway to the kitchen, the most luxurious bathroom and so on. Such self-expression is healthy and helps to maintain the enthusiasm of the group.

Occasionally however it can get out of hand as with the group who used different coloured mortar as a medium for self-expression. It's the one scheme I rarely revisit!

Yet self-expression is important — and it would be wrong for an architect to impose a strong or unusual design element on a client. It encourages innovation and this is essential to widen the self-builder's range of techniques and allow self-build to become a greater creative force in the housing field.

I think it is important to innovate in order to free self-build from its dependence on traditional building skills. Designs which require a lesser proportion of technical know-how enable more people without the necessary expertise and funding to benefit. There are a growing number of schemes now underway which reflect these concerns — I am thinking in particular of some of the timber frame constructions available — and trade dependent self-build, while still relevant, may become less dominant in the future.

Artist's impression of a self-built house in Cambridgeshire. Taken from plans by Design and Materials.

Demolishing their subsiding home and rebuilding on the same site was the most influential factor determining the design of the Dryboroughs' new self-build home. In their search for like-for-like they came up with something bigger and better...

Did the earth move for you?

Creating your own home can be a passionate affair but it's not every self-builder that gets to feel the earth move. That's what happened to the Dryboroughs during the long hot summers of 1975 and '76 — well before the idea of building for themselves was even considered.

The reason was massive subsidence to their three-bedroomed detached house in Hornchurch, Essex, as John Dryborough, a property surveyor in London, explains: 'The drought caused lots of problems for houses that were built on clay like ours. The clay dries out, the foundations move and the house subsides.'

The foundations had been underpinned, but unsuccessfully as it turned out. Ten years later, the most practical solution was to sell to a developer and find somewhere else to live. But after a week of house-hunting the Dryboroughs came to their senses. 'We thought what on earth are we doing? We like it here. We chose to live here. Years before when we were first married we talked about building our own home — and here was the opportunity presented to us on a plate.'

With the decision made, the first step was to come up with a design. The couple soon found that there is always somebody ready to offer advice — but not always of the right sort.

'Acquaintances offered to put some ideas down on paper and work out a scheme. But apart from being too expensive, we ended up with what *they* wanted rather than what we wanted.' It was during a visit to the local library to look at self-build case studies that John came across *Design and Materials*. Acting on a phone call, D and M sent a representative round to meet them.

'The company said just to scribble what we wanted on the back of an envelope and they would go away and do it properly — which they did. We were absolutely delighted with the plans when they came through.'

Then followed a fortnight of close scrutiny and modification to get the finished scheme right. The aim was to recreate their old home but with more space and extra rooms.

The site was relatively restricted — particularly its width at only 40ft. The new house was to be a similar shape but with the building line extended at the back by 8ft. Extra space was also created by having an integral rather than a detached garage, and by not having bay windows which in the old house occupied too much room.

The final design included a separate laundry room adjoining the kitchen, as well as two extra bedrooms.

John was adamant that the house would have to be maintenance-free: 'The old house was rendered which meant it had to be painted regularly. This was not just expensive but time-consuming and boring.' Brick was therefore chosen as the finish.

Once the design was finalised, D and M sorted out the necessary planning permission. It was then time to get down to work. The family moved to rented accommodation four miles away and within a week the old house was demolished by a local contractor.

Because of the subsidence the foundations had to be piled to a considerable depth. John had had to find a builder registered with the National House-Building Council who was prepared to use the shell materials supplied by D and M, and provide the labour and the extra materials himself. He found one locally who was prepared to do the job using his own sub-contractors and at a reasonable price.

The Dryboroughs hardly lifted a finger during the actual building but their continual presence on site was absolutely essential to oversee the work and keep up the pressure.

Says John: 'The construction industry isn't the most reliable. I used to go to the site almost every day on my way to work to see how things were going and spent a lot of time on the phone chasing things up.'

The materials were supplied in two basic consignments and if there was a problem with doing it like this, it was that perhaps too much was delivered all at once.

'It rather clogged the site up and you had to make sure someone was there to unload and say where they wanted everything put. It got to the stage where the front of the site was so blocked that it was becoming difficult to move,' said John.

Considering that the build was taking place in the middle of a suburban street — and not a building site — neighbours had every right to get upset. But

Choosing the best design
Case study

The Dryborough family home being demolished in preparation for their self-manage project

The new house as it now stands on the same site

diplomatic moves by John, which included writing to each one to explain what was happening and giving a contact number in case of problems, prevented any bad feeling. 'Fortunately they were very understanding — one actually made tea for all the workers one day. Considering the dust and the dirt they were really good.' Within six months the building work was complete. Plastering took place in January — not the best time of year because it takes a long time to dry out. By Easter however, the family had moved into their new home. All were delighted with the end result.

'People ask me if there's anything I would have done differently, but I can honestly say there isn't — at least not with the design of the house itself. I think if I did build again I'd try and tie the builder down a lot tighter. If he had stuck to the programme and worked continually on site we would have saved six or seven weeks.

'I would recommend self-build to anyone as long as they have the time and the money to do the things they want to do. If you're going to do it, don't try and do it on the cheap.'

BA

" We thought we'd start off with something simple "

...The best advice to any first-time self-builder is to keep the design simple...

7. What's the damage?

The Department of the Environment's prediction of 20,000 house starts by 1991 means that building societies are faced with the challenge of placing more importance on this relatively high-risk investment. DAVID AINLEY, Commercial Lending Manager for the National and Provincial, describes the workings and implications of the society's new package...

The way it used to be

The financial arrangements for a self-build project are the crux of any successful venture. The saving that an individual can make building his or her own home compared to buying on the open market, while acquiring a bigger or better house, provides the incentive.

Traditionally, the majority of financial institutions consider the individual self-build project to be in the high-risk category. Most building societies will lend money in instalments to finance the actual building work, but this has always been on the understanding that the self-builder would obtain an overdraft from a bank to purchase land and get started until the building society released an advance.

The overdraft, or bank bridging loan, is arranged with the bank taking a charge on the land and the provision of a personal guarantee. Another source of funds to purchase the site is when another form of security is offered, either a re-mortgage or a further charge on an existing home. Some individuals are prepared to sell their home and move their family into a caravan to raise the money for the site. Once a building society is aware of the proposed security, progress payments are released — usually in four instalments. Until the first payment arrives it may be difficult to pay for materials to start work on the building. The four stages of payment coincide with the completion of a damp-proof course, the roof, plastering and final touches on a house. These payments

A totally new idea Ug ... I'm calling it "self-build"

are only released upon receipt of confirmation by the society's valuer that the stage has been completed. As each stage payment is released, repayments are calculated and the self-builder is expected to start paying them immediately, together with any existing mortgage and possible overdraft interest.

100 per cent finance

In 1989 the National and Provincial introduced a new financial package for the self-builder. It is an innovative combination of development finance and long-term mortgage, and finances the purchase of land, building costs, professional fees and services.

Once the right applicant has been approved by the society, a loan of 100 per cent of the total cost is offered. The development period is expected to be up to 12 months — no repayments are required during this period — and interest that accrues to the loan will be capitalised at the end of the development. This assists the self-builder purchase the site then pay nothing until the house is completed and ready to move into. It enables self-builders to remain in their existing house, hopefully avoiding the trap of escalating house price inflation. Under the new arrangement money is released in six stages.

1. *Land acquisition.*
2. *Damp-proof course level.*
3. *Wall plate.*
4. *Roofed.*
5. *Plastered out.*
6. *Finished off.*

Once all the advance has been released, interest will be capitalised. The loan is then reduced, in line with any equity acquired when the self-builder's existing home is sold. The extent of the final mortgage is then dependent upon the society's criteria regarding the total earning power of the individual.

To obtain this finance, the self-builder must contact his or her local branch and set about convincing the society that the venture is going to be a success. We are not particularly interested in anyone's weird and wonderful approach. We want to see commitment, the ability to complete the project and manage the money released. So it is not just a case of assessing the scheme, but also the self-builder's personality and, of course, the ability to repay the loan at the end of the day. Once the right personal qualities have been assessed we then look in detail at the scheme.

Project control is essential. It is a condition of our package that the self-builder employs an architect or chartered surveyor to provide a full technical service including design, certification and management.

Questions asked

Having established who the professional consultants are, we then evaluate the following:

- **Where is the site?** *Any sketch plans, general information about the area. Who is the land being purchased from? Are there any conditions to the purchase? What planning details have been obtained? Have there been any detailed site investigations, such as soil reports?*
- **What type of property is being built?** *In particular we are looking at the marketability, what building materials are being used, and the method of construction. We need to see the plans and drawings that have been produced by the qualified architect.*
- **What is the building programme?** *It is obviously better to be excavating the foundations in spring with most of the outside work being done in the summer, leaving the winter months for the trades that will be concentrated indoors. This of course will depend on the weather, how much of the work is true self-build, how much of the work is sub-contracted, and where this fits into the building programme.*
- **What are the predicted costs?** *We look for detailed building costs, cash flows, bills of quantities, a sub-contract allowance, what plant needs to be purchased or hired, and so on. These are used as a basis to arrive at the final figure for the loan.*

This will provide sufficient information for the society to instruct its own valuer to visit the site for a valuation on the land and a valuation of the proposed building. He will also be called upon to make site inspections to confirm building progress.

Once the finance has been arranged, another condition of the society's package is insurance. This includes a life policy to cover the cost of building the house in the event of death with the building incomplete, insuring the building at all stages from storm and fire damage, and a public liability and contractor's all-risks insurance to cover workers and passers-by against any injury on site.

The National Provincial was intending to have this scheme available from all its branches from around mid-1989. ▶

Details of self-build insurance policies in Chapter Twelve. ▶

What's the damage?
Case study

The story of how Mike Eydman built Gable Fell is given in his own words beginning on page 99. Photographs on pages 92-93. ▶

When a former financial consultant sets out to build his own home, he can be expected to keep a keen eye on the budget. In Mike Eydmann's case this meant analysing costs as he went along. The figures relate to a four-bedroomed detached house in Garstang, Lancashire...

Where Mike's money went

The pie chart, *below*, gives a rough indication of where Mike incurred the cost of building Gable Fell, while the table overleaf gives a more detailed breakdown. Mike bought the land in 1987 and went for a timber frame package based on his own rough design, buying the frame and materials during 1988/89. Both friends and professional sub-contractors helped Mike in the building work and the tables list labour costs, legal fees and materials costs. VAT is excluded, as are fixtures and fittings, and garden landscaping. The chart on page 74 shows how the cost compares with the eventual value of the house.

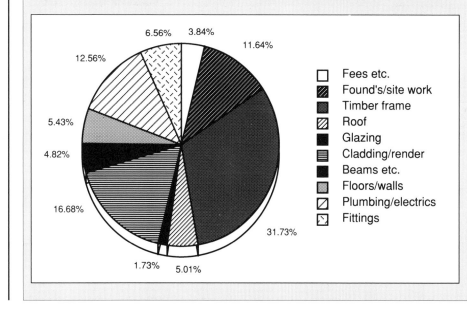

Legend:
- ☐ Fees etc.
- ▨ Found's/site work
- ■ Timber frame
- ▧ Roof
- ■ Glazing
- ▤ Cladding/render
- ■ Beams etc.
- ▨ Floors/walls
- ▨ Plumbing/electrics
- ⋈ Fittings

The cost of Gable Fell

	£	£	Proportion of cost
Fees and charges			
Builders risk insurance	125		
Planning fees (Prestoplan)	288		
Local authority fees	250		
Services — gas, water, electricity & telephone	492		
Architect's certificate	185		
	1,340	1,340	3.9%
Foundation and site works			
Foundation — materials	1,235		
— labour and machinery	1,436		
Fixing of sole plates	67		
Driveway (materials only)	169		
Paving for perimeter paths	180		
	3,087	3,087	8.9%
Drainage works			
Materials	444		
Labour, including machinery	530		
	974	974	2.8%
Timber frame			
Prestoplan package inc. insulation and fixings	10,424		
Additional timber	147		
Extra for internal doors	420		
Extra for turned balusters	75		
	11,066	11,066	31.7%
Roof			
Materials (inc. garage)	1,290		
Labour (main roof only)	350		
Guttering (materials only)	108		
	1748	1748	5.0%
Glazing			
Double glazed units inc. putty	605	605	1.7%
Exterior cladding			
Materials inc. bricks and blocks	2,078		
Labour inc. inglenook and chimney. Also includes use of builder's scaffolding	2,890		
	4,968	4,968	14.2%
Rendering			
Sand and cement etc.	84		
Labour	660		
Paint	105		
	849	849	2.4%

	£	£	Proportion of cost
Beams			
Exterior GRP beams to all elevations inc. garage	1,170		
Interior beams inc. sandblasting	201		
	1,371	1,371	3.9%
Inglenook fireplace			
Chimney materials excl. bricks	237		
Wood burning stove	306		
	543	543	1.6%
Internal walls and floor			
Plasterboard and sundries	876		
Materials for skimming	125		
Labour for skimming	600		
Floating floor (materials only)	294		
	1,895	1,895	5.4%
Heating and plumbing			
Central heating (materials)	1,463		
Labour (heating engineer)	460		
Plumbing (materials)	370		
Labour (plumbers)	574		
	2,867	2,867	8.2%
Electrics			
Materials	508		
Extractor fans	112		
Down lighters, wall lights, etc	199		
Security system (materials)	151		
	970	970	2.8%
Kitchen, utility and bathrooms			
Two, four-piece bathroom suites, cloakroom set and shower	888		
Kitchen and utility room units, sinks and worktops	660		
Wall tiles	149		
	1,697	1,697	4.9%
Wardrobes			
Built-in units to three bedrooms (materials only)	590	590	1.7%
Sundries			
Interior and exterior wood stain	262		
Nails, screws and sundries	48		
	310	310	0.9%
Total building costs		34,880	100.0%
NB — Outside labour content		7500	21.5%

THE SECRET OF
SUCCESS
IS IN THE
ORGANISATION

From start to finish.
Group Self-Build Housing Management.
A truly comprehensive service.

Land finding

Scheme design

Planning approvals

Costing

Project finance

Group selection

Association registration

Contract management

Project planning

Materials scheduling

Purchasing

Administration

New schemes are always
being planned.

For further information
please contact:

*Group Self-Build
Housing Management*

Limited services available to individual self-builders
but always excluding land finding.

HOMESMITH
CONSULTANTS

Telephone: 0274 870473
Homesmith plc Northfield Snelsins Road Cleckheaton West Yorkshire BD19 3UE

The bar chart shows how the cost of Gable Fell was divided between land and building work and puts into context the saving made when compared with a commercial valuation of the finished property.

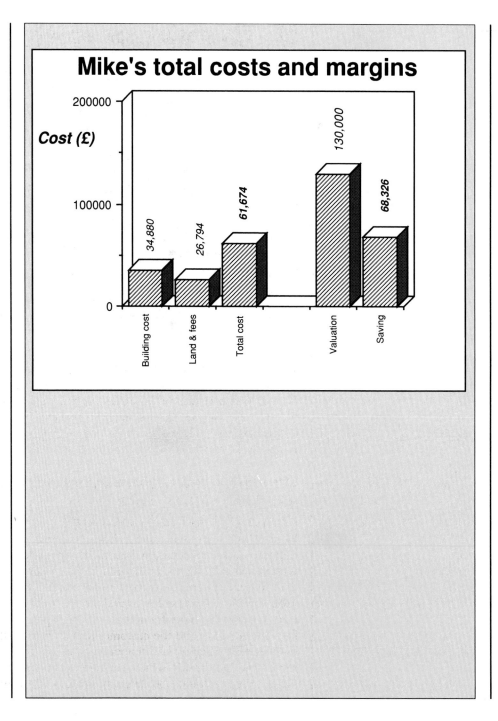

8. Breaking with tradition

Anyone who knows anything about self-build cannot help being sucked into the debate between traditional and timber-frame construction. While there are recognised advantages to both, most self-builders have their own reasons for choosing as they do. DAVID HOPPIT, property correspondent for The Daily Telegraph, **answers questions on his preference for a less 'traditional' approach...**

Which method of construction are you most in favour of?

Timber-frame every time. In the great Essex earthquake of April 1884, the houses least affected by the tremor, according to contemporary accounts, were those built of wood; likewise in more recent hurricanes. When it comes to extremes of temperature or natural phenomena we are safer, and snugger, in the embrace of timber.

Why then has there been a period of consumer resistance to a building system which has been tried and tested the world over, and found to be excellent?

Houses built today will have to last 1,000 years or more (at the present rate of replacement) and so they will certainly have numerous freak weather conditions with which to contend. In the mid 1970s timber-framed houses represented less than ten per cent of the market, but as the 1980s got into full swing that share grew rapidly until a peak was reached in which nearly one in three new homes in Britain had a timber-framed inner wall. The house builders found the system fast and efficient, and the customer probably had little idea whether the property he or she was buying had timber, or building block, inner walls; it looked the same from the outside whichever system was being used. Only by tapping on the inner walls could one detect whether block or timber had been used.

Above — *Stone-faced timber-frame house (Prestoplan)*

Left — *House built from traditional materials (RBS)*

Right — *Dormer-house of traditional materials (D and M)*
Below — *Timber-framed bungalow (Prestoplan)*

Breaking with tradition

JOAN RUSSELL

The Colton self-build group from Leeds (see page 81) — back row, from left: Bill Cavens, Thomas Turner, Trevor Ward, Cliff Whitehead, Pete Ryder, Barry Carr. Front: Joseph Clayton, John Ellis, Terry White and Martin Russell.

So why the hostility?

By 1983 the timber-frame share of the market had so alarmed the proponents of other forms of building, notably building blocks, that a vigorous and sometimes venomous anti-timber campaign was launched, culminating in a rather ill-researched TV documentary which focused on the problems allegedly caused by bad practice in the use of timber-frame by one major builder. Timber-frame was instantly branded as a highly dubious method of construction. The industry buried its head in the sand and volume house builders reverted to brick and block without a whimper of protest; it was a pathetic show of cowardice.

What has been done to redress the balance?

Within a few months of the *World in Action* programme, timber frame houses had been given a clean bill of health by the National House Building Council, the Building Societies Association, the fire brigades and the Building Research Establishment; but the damage had been done already. Closer investigation of the record of timber-frame properties revealed that they had 'performed' very much better than those of their opponents. The NHBC had received fewer than 30 complaints about timber-frame houses during a 20-year period prior to the programme, compared with 20,000 for block-built homes; true the share of the market was much smaller, but the disparity is significant for all that.

Did the campaign play on the ignorance of the consumer?

In my view yes — which is ironic when you think that at that time half a million families were already living in a timber-framed house. One builder at the time who offered buyers the choice of construction said some buyers thought timber-framed homes were little more than fortified garden sheds.

However, the slanging match which developed as a result of the saga did help to focus attention on one of the most important aspects of house building — the need for first-class site supervision during construction by whatever method. It is almost impossible to ascertain whether vapour and fire barriers are properly fitted (or indeed fitted at all) once the house is completed; a good site manager will keep an eagle eye on such matters.

What, then, are the advantages of using timber-frame?

Provided all the basic rules of construction are observed, the buyer of a house with an inner skin of timber should get a home which is more flexible and cheaper to heat than one with a block inner wall. The roof, too, is more easily fixed to a timber structure, giving better all-round integrity. Sound insulation should be better as well, and all that 'drying out' in a brick and block home is eliminated. The house is built faster, and therefore secured from light-fingered passers-by that much more swiftly. Scandinavians, who have no fossil fuels to fall back upon, and both North and South Americans, have all embraced timber construction, and find our resistance to it inexplicable.

Many of our great Tudor houses were built of timber, of course, but opponents of timber frame argue that they were 'hard' as opposed to 'soft wood'. This too is something of a misnomer (balsa is actually a 'hardwood'), for properly treated pine should last as long as oak. 'Open heart' surgery on timber-frame homes built nearly 30 years ago has revealed mint-condition wood behind the plaster board. Frames produced by firms such as Potton, Guildway, and Cartledge are servicing both self-build groups and established house-builders. Their products give a new home its own 'thermal underwear', making it both highly energy-efficient and fast to erect.

With so many positive features why isn't every self-builder using timber-frame?

Many are. Timber's share of the market has remained low so far as the numbers game is concerned; however, whereas it was the lower end of the market which was using the system to such good effect six years ago, it is the top range of houses which tends now to use the system. Even Barratt, perhaps the hardest hit of the major builders by the TV campaign, is now using more timber for its adventurous California range — large American-style houses having their first airing in England at Milton Keynes.

Is there a future in this method of construction?

The last decade of the century could prove a milestone for the timber and brick house, for a major revision of building regulations was expected during 1989; one of the aspects due to be covered was energy efficiency, an area where timber can more than hold its own.

Thermal insulation is measured in U-value, which is the boffins' way of measuring heat loss from a house. For the record, it is 'watts per square metre per degree centigrade' lost through walls, floors and ceilings. The current U-value required by the industry is 0.6, which is less efficient than the Swedes had achieved by 1945. Their houses now are down to 0.2 or less, achieved by wrapping some 24 centimetres of insulation around the house within the timber structure, and at the same time using a system which gives a complete change of air every two hours, the ducted warm stale air helping to warm the incoming fresh air. Double or even triple glazing is used, and with all the solar gain, the problem even in the bleakest winters can be getting rid of excess heat. Our weather does not perhaps demand quite such drastic measures, but we are a long way from reaching an acceptable level of efficiency in our homes; timber frames will play a major role in the quest for a perfect home.

PRESTOPLAN

Your number one choice

Because it takes more than ambition to build a home

Worldwide, over two million people choose timber frame every year. We at *Prestoplan* are flattered that so many discerning and experienced people within the housing and building industry settle for our timber frames when deciding on their new home. With over 20 years experience you can depend on *Prestoplan*.

REMEMBER!
- **We can adapt any design to your requirements**
- **Approved by the NHBC, Building Societies and Insurance Companies**
- **We offer a wealth of practical advice and help from initial contact to completion**
- **Our team of locally based area managers are ready to help you**

Talk to Prestoplan now, and soon you'll be looking forward to moving into your dream home!

PRESTOPLAN
The Professionals' Choice

England and Wales: Prestoplan Homes, Stanley Street, Preston, Lancashire, PR1 4AT ☎ (0772) 51628
Scotland: Prestoplan Homes, Strathaven, Lanarkshire, ☎ (0357) 20792
Northern Ireland: Prestoplan Homes by Woodbridge Homes, The Mews, Greenwood Manor, Greenwood Avenue, Belfast, BT4 3JJ ☎ (0232) 540329

When ten working individuals get together to build a brand new cul-de-sac for themselves — a job demanding constant commitment and a hefty loan — timing is an important factor. This explains their joint decision to use timber-frame...

Ten homes in nine months

With full-time jobs to keep on, and monthly interest repayments to be met, no-one wants their self-build project to linger any longer than necessary.

Which is where, for self-build groups especially, timber-framed housing comes into its own. The Colton self-build group in Leeds began work on site at Easter 1987, and the project was completed within schedule by the beginning of December.

A total of nine months, from the first spade hitting the ground to the tenth family moving in, isn't bad going and is the result, it would seem, of the group's decision to avoid traditional materials.

'The main reason why we chose timber-frame was to cut down on the amount of manual labour and time,' said group member John Ellis, a specialist in timber-frame construction who put his money where his mouth is. 'I reckon that without timber-frame we'd have been looking at a project three times as long.'

This decision, like many others, was made democratically by the committee, the self-build business being serious stuff. When you consider that for most of us house purchasing proves to be one of life's most traumatic experiences, then it's hardly surprising that those who build their own are keen to get it right. The Colton team made no exception.

To begin with, they hired an experienced consultant manager to secure land and finance on their behalf. The *Alliance Leicester Building Society* agreed to lend up to £500,000, and land was obtained from Leeds City Council.

Nor was there anything arbitrary about selection procedures — the ten were chosen from a range of applications, after extensive interviewing and the careful balancing of personnel. It was important to get a selection of tradesmen and some people with managerial skills. The result was a motley crew of bricklayers, electricians, plumbers, and joiners. There were two *white collars* among them — a surveyor and John. Running the site day-to-day was Trevor Ward who was looking forward to living, as well as working, with his neighbours.

'We're all couples, and most of us have kids. Most are no older than 40, so we should be a young, friendly neighbourhood.'

During the build, differences of opinion were dealt with at regular site meetings. Rules and regulations were devised and accepted by majority vote with fines for lateness and unjustified absenteeism: 'It's no good staying at home every time your back aches,' said one of the team. 'We all agreed to do at least 30 hours a week so there wasn't much time for lying in.'

Although each builder drew lots for his personal plot, the group adhered to a sequence of progressive building. This ensured that they all remained motivated, working collectively until the end. As an incentive to keep going, fairly and without it becoming a race, it was written into the members' contracts that as families moved in they would pay a 'rent' equivalent to the mortgage repayment into group funds. The mortgages were released together on the day the tenth family moved in.

The fact that the frame was erected so quickly meant that internal work began within days, with the builder no longer at the mercy of the weather. To make the best use of the specialised labour, everyone stuck to what they knew best, whether it was electrical work, plumbing or joinery.

Having said this, they were equally good at mucking in and general labouring jobs like mixing concrete, laying foundations, and doing the million and one heavy, dirty, difficult jobs that go into building a house were shared without resentment.

Members felt that the rigidity of the timber-frame structure allowed for a high degree of accuracy with straight lines and neat angles. As one of the group said: 'The frame acts as a mould to build around which makes it more appropriate for the layman. You don't need to be an expert to build your own timber-framed house. As long as you've got a few practical skills and a bit of sense then you're all right.'

While individuals were unlikely to drop out because the work was too technical, there was always the problem of personal disagreements. After all, not many of us spend up to 30 hours a week in such close proximity to all our neighbours.

'We had our moments,' admitted John Ellis. 'But generally we get on really well. Certainly the mothers do — they were all out together in the evenings while we were slaving away.'

The wives had a crucial role to play on site at weekends, working hard providing drinks and snacks for their partners. It was not uncommon for the women to help with the building work too, and while the Colton women managed

Some women do an awful lot more than make tea! See Chapter Ten. ▶

Breaking with tradition

Case study

to keep their hands clean, many were involved in the nitty gritty of committee meetings and initial decision making. Within a few months of building everyone felt at home on the site. They had their own milkman and were all known at the corner shop.

The combined result of the group's nine-month slog was a million pounds worth of housing — not bad for a spare-time job. And the effort didn't go unnoticed by the media, with pieces in the local press and a slot on regional television.

So how does it feel to be a star? 'It's great. We've done us all proud,' boasted Trevor Ward who said the new homes 'look just like Brookside'. His four-bedroomed house, he described as 'just beautiful' with 'full mod cons including radio-controlled garage and a power shower' — ideal for washing away the after-effects of a monumental party the group had to celebrate the last person moving in.

And all certainly had much to celebrate. As well as owning a brand new home and having the satisfaction of a job well done, their houses, costing less than half their final value, represented a major financial investment.

It's not just the money, though, as John Ellis proudly points out: 'We've built a new neighbourhood for our families, a smarter way of life.'

JS

John Ellis (left) and Trevor Ward

It may seem surprising to find a qualified plasterer — aware of the convenience of timber-frame requiring only dry-lining — building his own house in traditional materials.
Experienced in both methods of construction, Neil Quantick is confident that when he built his family home in Ebbw Vale he made the right choice...

Sticking with what you know

One influence behind Neil Quantick's decision to use traditional materials was a friend recommending *Rationalised Building Systems*, a package firm based in Cardiff. Neil had seen enough mistakes doing contract work on commercial sites to remind him that the best way to operate is by word of mouth.

Money was another factor. The Quanticks initially were keen to have a timber-frame home, mainly because of the high level of insulation, but when they priced up the spacious design they had in mind, the package for the timber-frame equivalent came out around £2,000 dearer.

Many feel that this additional building expense is more than outweighed by the shorter building time and cheaper labour costs of timber-frame, together with its efficient insulation guaranteed to reduce running costs permanently.

Neil Quantick begged to differ. Because he was doing most of the building work himself, labour costs were not an important consideration, and he was confident that with six-inch thermal blocks, three-inch cavities, and glass fibre wadding between the first and second floor, he could be assured of adequate insulation.

He also believed that with tight organisation, and a professional attitude he could erect a traditionally built house almost as quickly as a timber-frame one. He set out to plan the work so that he could build at the same time as the few contractors he took on, and aimed for a 'fast, tidy job'.

This he achieved in just over six months, beginning in August 1987, reaching the roof by September the same year, and moving in during January and February the following year. Other tradesmen were Neil's work contacts

— typically bartering 'a job for a job'. This kept costs low and for £45,000 (including land at £7,000) the Quanticks now have a luxury four-bedroomed detached house built to lavish taste, and already worth double its cost.

Neil Quantick is convinced that more people should look into the possibility of self-build. He was introduced to the idea during a passing conversation with a stranger at a friend's wedding reception.

'He didn't know the first thing about the building trade, and that got me thinking. I felt ashamed and said to Karen, 'If he can do it then why can't I?'

Karen Quantick is not without her talents either. So that Neil could carry on earning through the week, she and their two-year-old daughter visited the site every day to organise deliveries and help out. Her jobs included staining all the woodwork inside, and out, unloading materials, and preparing the inside of the house by tiling and decorating.

Neil's methodical approach paid off in the long run. 'I would recommend that anyone trying this for the first time should work out an order of completion and stick to it, ordering materials before they are needed.'

Sticking to a check list often meant juggling workmates around, and informing them of any delays so that the Quanticks didn't miss their slot. Said Neil: 'No subbie is going to sit around waiting at your convenience. You have to ring them up constantly and let them know if you're running late. Otherwise by the time you're ready, three weeks behind schedule or whatever, they've every right to turn round and say they can't come for another two months.'

The Quanticks had the advantage of buying council land with the services already connected. The council provided them with a rented flat for the duration of the building work, which allowed them to sell their existing home in advance, and buy the site and materials for the rafted foundations before taking out a mortgage.

Being self-employed could have made getting a mortgage difficult, but at least Neil had the foundations as evidence that he meant business. 'Once the mortgage company could see that I wasn't going to fail, they came up with the money. And the package service was invaluable because it meant that we could have the goods before paying. I don't know if this is usual, but RBS was marvellous with us.'

The Quanticks learnt that it was wise to borrow slightly more than the costings suggested. 'There's nothing worse than moving in and then having to scrimp and save just to buy a picture or a carpet. It's easy to overspend just in small cash jobs. Twenty pounds here and there on nothing in particular soon grows into a few hundred pounds that can't be accounted for.'

Karen kept a close track of this, as she handled the VAT receipts. 'You've got to keep them all in a logical order because they soon mount up.' Indeed, with an estimated VAT return of £3,000 the Quanticks are planning to build a garage

Breaking with tradition

Case study

Neil and Karen Quantick with their daughter Danielle, now four

and finish landscaping the patio and garden.

As yet that's as far as their future plans go. They would consider self-build again, but only if the right plot came up. Both feel that the combination of privacy at the back with an open view makes it one of the best sites in the district.

But if the time comes, it looks like being another RBS package. 'Nothing was too much trouble to them,' said Karen. 'When I broke a window by slamming one of the doors they replaced it free of charge even though it was my fault.'

Neil was particularly impressed with the way RBS incorporated his and Karen's ideas into the design. Alterations included open-plan stairs with a stained glass picture window, an archway through to the dining room, and the opening up of storage space in the kitchen.

Official approval helped them to keep going. Both the local authority building inspector and a surveyor came to inspect Neil's work at intervals (a prerequisite of any mortgage is that the house must be certified by an independent surveyor) which proved an important boost to morale. 'There are so many firms out to help the self-builder these days, I seem to spend all my time telling others to have a go. My advice to anyone is really quite simple,' said Neil, 'do it.'

JS

*...From now on there is the
unpredictable weather to take
into account...*

9. Getting out on site

HOWARD SCHOFIELD is Co-director of Zoneworth Ltd — *a property redevelopment company based in Buxton, Derbyshire. A qualified civil engineer who built his own house in 1984, he is responsible for the on-site management of the Zoneworth schemes. He combines his professional and personal viewpoint to offer invaluable practical advice to the self-builder...*

Making lists

At last! The day has arrived that you thought never would. You can start 'real' work. All those frustrating, delaying, time-consuming rules and regulations have at last been satisfied.

To have reached this stage clearly demonstrates your determination to succeed. You are obviously survivor material. But what you have experienced is only the beginning. So far, problems have been organisational ones. From now on there is the unpredictable British weather, and the fact that you will now start to spend money at an alarming rate, to take into account. Careful planning at this stage to overcome anticipated problems will therefore pay handsome dividends.

Planning falls into two parts. The emergency plan and the preferred plan. The emergency plan makes sure that you end up with a successful project — that is a completed house — come what may. So it is essential to prepare for the unexpected.

A building site is a tough environment especially for those not used to it. Be ready to deal with the problems of accident or sickness. If any of these unfortunate things happen you can guarantee that it will be at the most inconvenient time, usually when you have committed yourself to considerable expenditure. This plan is neither your easy way out, nor an escape route when things get tough. It is the plan that gives you the peace of mind so that you know that no matter what happens, your survival plan will ensure a successful project. The preferred, or detailed, plan is the framework for decisions and action. It is also the base for measuring all progress. During your earlier work on the design and financial planning you will already have undertaken a considerable amount of detailed analysis. You will probably be familiar with bar charts for your cash flow calculations. Use this same logic in greater detail to determine the resources and materials required for each activity. Normally in the building trade, resources would mean the labour and main equipment. With self-build, it means labour, certainly (mainly you), and every last bit of equipment or services you or your sub-contractor will need.

For the inexperienced, it is probably a waste of time to try to analyse the whole job in one go. It is also very frustrating to do a lot of tedious, involved administrative work and then to find in a very short time that it is all wrong. Building work is a very complex business even for the experts, and at this stage you are only the apprentice. By the time you have finished the decorating stage you will be among the experienced, if not the expert. Despite the difficulties, it is vital that some serious attempt is made at detailed forward planning.

Begin at the beginning — the foundations. List the labour and skills required. Work out the quantities of materials needed. Calculate the various floor areas and keep these handy as you will use this basic information many times. Identify all the supporting materials that are required: damp-proof course material, damp-proof membrane, an assortment of nails and screws, secondary timber for profiles and shuttering. These are just a few examples. The more thorough the list, the better your performance on site.

Having used this data to start the job, then keep a diary of events. The experience you gain in achieving this stage will provide an excellent base from which you can plan the next step. The beauty of this gradual approach is that not only does the planning become easier and more accurate, but there is a great sense of achievement at the start. You will have planned a major activity and made it happen. You will probably have made some mistakes, but this is all part of the learning curve.

Practical planning

The best boost for morale is always to get down to some work. Once out on site there are essential requirements which need to be satisfied. As we have said before, the building environment is rugged, if not downright rough. You will work long hours and get wet, cold, hungry and tired. It is therefore of paramount importance to look after personal needs first.

Although it may be embarrassing to talk about basic needs, it is infinitely more embarrassing if facilities are not available when needed! Toilets are top of the list. Modern caravan techniques and simple screening are all that are required.

Next, you will need shelter. My work started with my car as the site office. With only a small increase in manpower we quickly graduated to an old garage which was still on site. If all else fails, buy a prefabricated site hut which at a later date can always be used as a garden shed. It is now that you will begin to notice that the funds are rapidly going down. At this preliminary stage don't worry. Invest willingly, but carefully. The facilities you create will last all through the building period and will see you through the tough patches.

The personal shelter during winter should have some form of heating. Dry, unheated shelter is also required for the numerous items on the material lists. With timber-frame construction there is often the need to take delivery of large quantities of materials at the same time. Plaster boards, insulation materials, door sets and pre-glazed window frames are just some of the items. If immediate storage is not available it would be helpful to have standby arrangements ready in advance. Friends may have lock-up garages that are no longer in use. Farmers may well have huge sheds that are often under used. The ideal is to find the space you need with the flexibility to come and go as you please.

It is also a good idea to invest in a complete set of waterproof clothes. A heavy, waterproof jacket, leggings, the inevitable gum boots with steel toe caps, and, of course, a pair of stout working boots are all essential items. Never wear ordinary boots and shoes. You will inevitably be involved in heavy lifting when you are cold and tired. It is then when an accident is waiting to happen and steel toe caps can save you from a lot of pain and possible job delay.

General site planning

The next piece of practical planning is to establish the general site layout. Obviously, the layout of the foundations takes priority but there are other things worth considering.

Check the access to the site and make sure it is suitable for heavy articulated lorries. If there are valuable stone gate posts or the opening is narrow, take out one or both posts and provide firm access with hardcore.

During construction topsoil is a real nuisance. During wet weather it is messy and sticky and in any weather it is far too soft to take any real loads. It is also not recommended to have organic materials under your house. On the other hand, when the job is complete topsoil is obviously essential for the garden which will display your masterpiece of a house to perfection. It is therefore advisable to strip all the topsoil from your building area and store the spoil on one side for later recovery. The area uncovered should include the house site and two or three metres around the edge.

The sheer quantity of earth that comes out once the foundation dig begins

Slowly but surely it took Mike Eydmann from July 1987 to March 1989 to build his four-bedroomed mock-Tudor timber-frame house in Lancashire. It was never intended to take so long, but — as is so often the case with self-build schemes — injuries and business commitments got in the way. See page 99 for the full story...

July 1987 — digging and laying the foundations

August 1987 — the foundations are complete and the sole plates fixed

September 1987 — first floor panels of the timber frame are erected

Above — *September 1987 and the roof construction is finished*

Above right — *view from the bedroom window*

Right — *the roof loaded out by October 1987*

July 1988 — at last, after a long break from building work, the garage roof and porch are constructed and some of the external beams in place never fails to take the inexperienced by surprise. Once disturbed, the earth 'bulks up' to a volume two or three times its original. This can produce real problems. Nowadays single-plot building sites are often congested or awkward. Under these circumstances it is highly recommended that arrangements be made to remove the earth from site as it is being dug out. This may mean hiring a mechanical digger and driver to carry out the excavation with supporting transport to remove bulk earth. The aim is for a 'clean' site. This will pay handsome dividends throughout the rest of the job.

Finding supplies

Typically, the bulk materials for the building will be specified in the drawings and documents, but information is limited. The industry generally assumes that builders are experienced and will find practical solutions to many constructional problems. It also assumes that they will have easy access to the massive range of building materials.

Until recently this posed problems for the private individual. But the DIY superstores have changed all that. The range and quality of the equipment they offer make it possible for any self-builder to deal quickly with the logistics of ordering dozens of different supplies.

Even if a superstore is available locally it is also advisable to set up account arrangements with one or two local builders' merchants. The availability of just what you want when you want it can be crucial, so it is best to have alternative supply sources readily available.

Similar investigations should be made for tool hire, plant hire and transport contractors. Locate the local joinery works. Find out about two or three local bricklayers, joiners, plumbers and electricians. At this stage you may mean to do all the work yourself but sometimes it is advisable to call in the experts — especially when time is running out. This preliminary investigation will ensure you have a good chance of getting help when you most need it.

Finally, set up your arrangements to get rid of rubbish. You will create a great deal of waste. Either use the ubiquitous skip, which is highly convenient, or use your trailer and the local tip. Your materials are unlikely to be classified as trade waste so it is possible that all your tipping would be free — but this will depend on the area.

Setting out

Positioning and setting out the outlines of your house is probably the first *real* step forward for the self-builder. It is advisable to get professional help at this early stage since you may need to use specialist levelling or surveying equipment. It is also useful to establish the outline dimensions very accurately — especially with timber-frame construction.

In the technical books you will have seen diagrams of profiles at each corner of an open trench. This gives an idea of the principles you must follow, but the practice is very different. During setting-out ensure that each marker is positioned well away from the digging area. They should be reasonably permanent and accessible over soil stacks. With mechanical diggers used for site clearance and trench excavation, any marker in the immediate vicinity will be completely destroyed. It is therefore essential to be able to set up string lines frequently and easily so that wall and trench positions can be monitored continuously.

For the actual digging operation, set out the trench centre line on the ground with sand or sawdust. Once the dig has been completed the local profiles can be established from the master controls.

Foundations and footings

Remember that the foundations are the root of the house. If it's a quality house you are after, then this is not the place for short cuts. A mistake made with foundations will probably not be realised until much later and the problems can then be both severe and expensive. Take expert advice on the design, especially if the foundations are near to trees or other buildings. It will give you great peace of mind to know that the start of your building is right.

It is also recommended that you check how the various services such as gas, water, electricity, drains and telephone are to enter the building. With modern designs, drains are within the house itself so there is a real need to provide suitable outlet points either through the walls or the actual foundations. It is much easier to build these in during construction rather than knocking holes in the structure as an afterthought.

With foundations cast, the footings are next. This is where the need for accurate setting-out becomes clear. With traditional brick and block there is an appreciable degree of tolerance that can be accommodated by skilled bricklayers. With timber-frame construction the outline dimensions — and especially the diagonals across the corners, which ensure that the building is square — must be accurate to a very fine degree. The timber-frame manufacturer will specify his tolerances and these must be strictly observed.

General points and safety

The remaining work should be planned in sections again — ensuring that the right materials and supplies arrive on time. Always remember: no materials, no progress — but the expense marches on.

With the analysis of each section you will also be able to decide the sort of skilled help you will need to support your own efforts. It is almost certain that just when you find you need skilled help is also the time when everyone seems

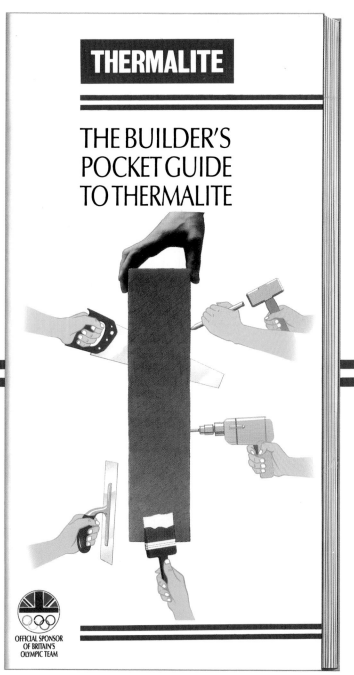

Getting out on site

to be too busy to lend a hand. Your previously established list of contacts will come in handy when shopping around.Without being dramatic, it is vital to recognise the need for sensible, as well as statutory, safety precautions. If you employ helpers or craftsmen on site you pick up special responsibilities. In particular, check that you have the correct and adequate insurance cover. Your solicitor or your insurance broker will list the minimum requirements and provide leaflets which explain the cover provided.

Read also the leaflets and recommendations issued by the Health and Safety Executive and follow these very straightforward commonsense rules. Remember the sensible clothing and wear steel toe-capped boots at all times. Use 110-volt hand power tools and lighting systems. Scaffolding in particular requires great care, with sound planks, handrails and toe boards.

...The sheer quantity of earth that comes out once the foundation dig begins, never fails to take the inexperienced by surprise...

When businessman Mike Eydmann and family moved north in 1985 it was with a view to fulfilling two special ambitions: one to build their own house, the other to build a car. With the car now complete, and the house almost ready, Mike writes his own story which begins in spring 1987...

Straight from the horse's mouth!

My wife Ann and I had set our hearts on a specific plot of land in Garstang, Lancashire, but as fate would have it, it did not come on the market for two years. This period allowed my other ambition, the car, to be designed and built. In the spring of 1987, we successfully tendered for the land and having achieved one ambition and overcome the first major hurdle of the other, we settled in at Ann's parents and work on the house began in earnest.

We had done our homework carefully and it became apparent to us fairly early on that the best way of achieving our goal was to build a timber-framed house. As non-tradesmen, it would enable us to participate more in the actual construction than would have been the case in a brick/block house, and the speed at which we could have a watertight shell in a part of the country not exactly noted for its dry climate was another plus point.

It also seemed logical to avoid wet trades. Why put over 1,000 gallons of water into the building and then have the problem of drying it out before decoration when it can be avoided in the first place? But it was the inherent energy efficiency of timber-frame that clinched it. Friends of ours have managed comfortably in their timber-framed house with only partial central heating backed up by a wood-burning stove — which can only be cheaper in the long run.

Having decided on timber-frame, I think we contacted every manufacturer in the country to see what the market had to offer. It is important at this stage to get a firm idea of how much budget you have available to build your new home. We rejected some manufacturers on grounds of style but rather more

Photographs of the timber-frame house being built are on pages 92-93.

$\blacktriangleright$

Listed in Chapter Twelve.

Detailed costings of Mike Eydmann's house are on page 71.

See table opposite.

on cost. Our budget was strictly limited and cost was a primary consideration. The next stage was to decide what sort of house we wanted. Building your own is a marvellous opportunity to get exactly what you want. We sat down and made a list of features we wanted in our new home. While some of the 'off the peg' designs met some, but not all, of our needs they tended to be beyond our budget.

The idea of designing our own home came from an excellent book by the Timber Research and Development Association. It tells you just what can and can't be done to keep costs down by designing the dwelling and timber-frame together. Eventually, we came up with a house incorporating everything we wanted within a floor area of 1,554 square feet, excluding the garage. Of course, there were compromises. The kitchen got larger as my study got smaller, and the utility room ended up pinching a corner of the garage, but we were both pleased by the end result. Generally speaking, the bigger the house, the more expensive it will be to build so it is wise at the design stage to divide the available construction budget by a realistic cost per square foot to determine the maximum affordable size.

We soon learnt that you can save money by shopping around for quotations. In our case, we sent exactly the same set of drawings to a shortlist of six manufacturers. When we received their quotes, they invariably needed adjusting to a common base before comparison. For instance, some included the garage door, others did not. The same was true for insulation, vapour barrier and nails and a whole lot of items. These all cost money so we had to add or delete them 'to compare apples with apples'.

We also drove as far as Dorset to look at examples of the different manufacturers products to assure ourselves of their quality. Our conclusions were that they all offered a very high standard of workmanship but with similar timber-frame packages ranging in price from £11,676 to £14,832. This was a difference of £3,156, or 27 per cent, for exactly the same thing. The only way we could decide on a package was to list those items most important to us, and eliminate those which could wait.

Once the specification and quotes were sorted out, the order for the kit was placed — in our case with *Prestoplan Homes.* They submitted planning and building applications for us and once planning permission was obtained, we were able actually to commence work. I raise my hat to those who undertake everything from digging foundations to installing the door bell. I admit to being far less heroic. We chose to bring in professional help where the budget allowed it or where we did not feel we had the necessary skills. It is always a difficult balance: bringing in tradesmen buys time as the job proceeds quicker, but it also chews into the money quicker than it will often allow.

Our first professional helper arrived in impressive style, armed with JCB

Getting out on site

Case study

Sorting out priorities is an important aspect of budget planning. Mike and Ann Eydmann's list shows some of the sacrifices they had to make, and how they prepared for possible modifications in the future.

Things that could wait...

● **Luxury bathroom** — To change a bathroom suite is no major problem if the layout is well designed in the first place. We opted for economy priced suites. If later we decide to buy more expensive suites and fittings, all the wastes and plumbing are in situ *and the job will be easy.*

● **Luxury kitchen** — Our kitchen and utility units cost us £422 as they were at the economy end of the range. We could have paid anything up to £3,000 for the 'top of the range'. We carefully thought out the layout of the kitchen so everything is where it should be. If we decide to change later, we can simply swap wall and floor units for more expensive ones without major upheaval.

● **Luxury appliances** — Appliances are modular so it is easy to instal a base cupboard where you want, say, a dishwasher. We made sure the power points, plumbing and wastes were there ready to receive them.

● **Electrical sockets and switches** — All ours are plastic but we wanted brass. It is such an easy job to change them later that we decided they could wait. We did not, however, skimp on the number of sockets. Nothing is guaranteed to ruin the William Morris wallpaper better than deciding you need another power point.

Things that could not wait...

● **Doors** — We deleted the sapele-faced doors from the kit and provided our own panelled softwood doors. They cost us more, but the thought of changing 14 doors at a later date was too daunting.

● **Double glazing** — We had 168 separate window panes and we were amazed at how little extra over single-glazing they cost. With the timber-frame being so thermally efficient, it is worth the extra to avoid the condensation problem.

● **Architraves and skirting boards** — Cheaper profiles were available but it's the sort of item you never change even if you wish you could.

● **Stairs** — A staircase with turned newel posts and balusters would have cost us an extra £500 on top of the kit price. We compromised by retaining the standard square newel posts and got a local wood turner to make us turned balusters for £75. Again, ripping out unsatisfactory balusters is not a job to be tackled once the decorating has been done.

and bulldozer. As soon as the foundations were dug, it rained and they filled with water. This is obligatory. As soon as they had dried out they were concreted and the construction taken up to floor slab level. At this stage I helped as labourer but we had decided to employ 'Mick the Brick' to set out the foundations, prepare them ready for the timber frame and subsequently to do all the drainage works, brickwork and blockwork. Mick proved to be worth his weight in gold.

Having made sure that the slab was spot on — essential to ensure that the frame stands accurately — we arranged to have the sole plates delivered before the rest of the kit. I hired a gun to shot-fire the fixings into the floor slab. We had a spell of glorious weather before the kit was due, until August 26th 1987 that is, when it came on the back of a 40ft trailer accompanied by torrential rain.

We had called on friends to help unload and they reminded us that it is a good idea to unload in some sort of order. The driver will invariably be in a hurry which makes it difficult to resist the temptation just to get everything off the trailer as it comes. This way, the first panel requiring erection will probably be at the bottom of the pile. We familiarised ourselves with the panel layout beforehand, and I would strongly recommend others to do the same.

If you can build a house of cards, you can build a timber-framed house. The cards are just bigger and weigh a lot more. This is when you discover who your friends really are. You do need help — unless you are prepared to pay for the manufacturer's erection service. We paid our friends with cans of 'amber nectar' and the house went up in the space of a few days — pausing only while I checked the dreaded diagonals to ensure all was square. I found it easier to instal the perimeter plasterboard noggins on all the ground floor panels prior to fitting the first floor deck. The alternative is to fit them afterwards — and rather you than me.

The construction of the house proved to be straight forward enough. Prestoplan supplied very good drawings and a build manual, and together with the sound building practice which came from Mick the Brick aided and abetted by our friendly local building inspector, there were no real problems. But it's never a piece of cake. Some jobs are dirty, heavy and wet. I will never forget working on the roof construction in late summer 1987. The rain was sheeting down, I was working alone, the water had penetrated my waterproofs which were restricting movement. I was tired and very, very unhappy. Unless the budget allows you to pay others to do the dirty work, I guess all self-builders will have their fair share of miserable days too.

And there were a few minor mishaps which made the insurance premiums worthwhile! There was the time I got careless and nearly sawed off my thumbnail instead of a plasterboard noggin for example; and New Year's Eve when I tore a leg muscle putting insulation down in the loft, and because the staircase had not been fitted, had to negotiate a rather unstable ladder. The balancing and swearing apart, the incident left me walking with a stick for a month.

Then there was an abortive attempt at doing away with the house, and the neighbours, all together. The garage gable end was built without putting in metal straps tying it to the roof trusses. I knew they needed fitting but as it would only be dangerous in the rare occurance of a strong east wind, and as there seemed to be a thousand and one more important jobs to do, I'm afraid it got left. That is until the windy Sunday afternoon when my neighbour interrupted Sunday lunch to ask me to remove my garage from their drive as they could not get the car out. Fortunately we were, and still are, friends, but it does not bear thinking about what could have happened. It was a silly and totally unneccessary accident proving the truth in the old saying 'never put off till tomorrow'...

Talking of roofs, Ann was convinced I would fall off and kill myself, and insisted on a professional to tile the main area. This cost £350 — which she figures was money well spent to avoid being widowed. We did not tile the garage roof until about six months later and I did this myself, but having done the job and watched others do it for me, I would recommend finding the extra budget to bring in the professional.

Ironically, a disadvantage of building timber-frame is the very speed of construction in the early stages. In a few short months we had the external appearance of a finished house but the inside was just a bare shell with open stud partitions. We found the internal work, because we did most of it ourselves, was painfully slow sometimes and you can easily get dispirited. We did not want to rely on cavity wall fixings and so we have tried to instal noggins for everything which meant more money and time. It means, for instance, deciding where the toilet roll holder is to be before dry-lining the wall. We tackled this job ourselves too. I think Ann is still recovering from the day we unloaded a lorry full of 190 8ftx 4ft sheets of plasterboard, and I am still amazed by the 50 kilograms of 40mm nails it took to put it all up.

Although we fitted the plasterboard ourselves, I did not feel I had the skill to make a really good job of the jointing. I got quotes for the entire job of dry-lining but I was not happy at what I was being asked to pay. In the end, we had the whole lot skimmed with Veneer Finish plaster which is specially made by British Gypsum. As only a 2mm thick coat is applied, it is dry and ready for decoration in a couple of days.

We wanted a heavily beamed interior to add character to the house. Rather than use new timber, I bought 650 ft of roof timbers from a factory demolition site in Blackpool. The finished effect is very pleasing. I fitted them myself but much of the second-fix joinery was done by my father-in-law. As a time-served joiner he was meticulous in his work and despite being in his 70s, can work many a younger man to a standstill.

The only thing I think I would do differently another time is the plumbing. I simply do not enjoy it, so I brought in a plumber and heating engineer. I suppose I just don't like soldering copper joints as I look on each of them as a potential weak point. Next time I would use an all plastic system which I now realise is more appropriate for use in timber-frame construction. As there are far fewer joints and the connections are just push fit I wouldn't bother using a sub-contractor.

One interesting detail on construction I am quite proud of is our external beams. The mock-tudor theme required feature timbers. I was very unhappy about using timber because unless you use oak or a hardwood, they need coating with wood preservative every two or three years. This in itself would be a very expensive and time-consuming maintenance job. I was also worried about water ingress behind the timber, caused by movement between the cement render and the beam. To overcome this, we had the areas to be rendered constructed in blockwork. After rendering and painting the entire surface, I developed a system of glass fibre 'timbers' using experience gained with glass reinforced plastics when developing my car bodywork. I manufactured production moulds and then the beams themselves. They are totally maintenance-free as they can not rot, and — being self-coloured — never need painting.

Their light weight made them easy to fix with special screws giving the appearance of studs. They are used to conceal telephone and burglar alarm wires and should the rendering require repainting, the fixings can be slackened enough to pull them away from the render to avoid painstaking 'cutting in'. Because they are fixed on, the problem of water ingress no longer applies. They initially cost us more than softwood timbers but when compared with oak, and taking into account the savings on future maintenance, they were much cheaper.

Was it worth it financially? The answer is an emphatic 'yes'. When I started in 1987 I judged the market value of the completed house to be between £80,000 and £85,000. In January 1989 an estate agent valued the house at around £130,000.

The dramatic increase in the value of the house reflects the volatile market during 1988, but I have not noticed the cost of labour and building materials rising by any appreciable amount in this same period. Self-build is therefore a certain way of getting a lot more for your money. All the incentives are there and my advice to anyone is to go ahead. There will be the disappointments and the downfalls, but these are far outweighed by the overall more satisfying feeling that everything is going well. Soon to move in, we have agonized so much over

More information on the synthetic beams available from Mike Eydmann's business — *Maelstrom Lancaster,* Caton Road, Lancaster. ▶

Getting out on site

Case study

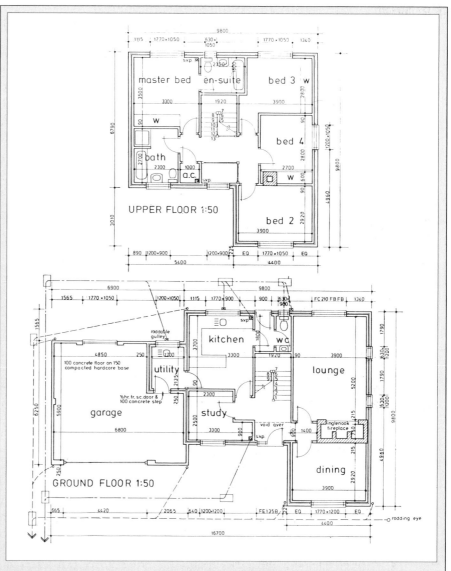

Prestoplan's interpretation of Mike and Ann's design

what to call our new home that naming it has proved to be more trouble than actually building it. But our neighbours and friends with the dented driveway have solved the problem. 'Why not call it Gable Fell,' they suggested. 'You overlook the Pennines and your blasted garage gable fell onto our perishing drive after all!'

ME

As part of the three-week course run by Constructive Individuals, Sue Miles, a health visitor with no previous building experience, worked on a house at Milton Keynes

10. Women in self-build

GAIL COUNSELL, *property correspondent with* The Independent, *is conscious that women are sadly under-represented on the majority of self-build group schemes. But the future holds some hope, as she discovers new self-build training courses which are attracting a healthy proportion of women...*

Self-build is about providing an inexpensive route to home-ownership. Women make up the fastest growing group of house buyers. Yet women are conspicuous by their absence when it comes to active participation in self-build schemes. No statistics are available but anecdotal evidence suggests that women make up at most no more than one or two per cent of the members of self-build schemes.

That is not to say, of course, that women do not currently have a part to play in self-build. But their role is probably summed up in the words of one scheme consultant who commented: 'The position of the women in the schemes is more to be supportive of their husband or boyfriend. After all she probably won't see anything of him at the weekend for the next 18 months.'

It must be questionable whether the situation is healthy as far as building relationships — or communities — is concerned, never mind houses. Yet the roots of this sexual demarcation appear, as is so often the case, to be primarily historical and structural rather than practical.

The common explanation for the poor showing made by women in self-build schemes is that most schemes require more than half their members to have experience of relevant trades — plumbing, electrical or bricklaying skills, for example. As women are thinly represented in these areas they are rarely in a position to apply to join schemes.

'Traditionally, self-build groups have been set up by building tradesman getting together and building houses,' says Roland Ashley, who handles self-build issues for the National Federation of Housing Associations. 'The absence of women reflects the industry.'

In reality, however, that provides only a partial explanation of why women fail to become actively involved. It does not, for example, explain why women are not to be found among the unskilled workers. Labouring, it is often argued, is heavy and dirty work. But so is carrying shopping, moving furniture, changing nappies or cleaning floors.

Rather, it seems, it is the attitudes of both women and men to the 'suitability' of females for certain kinds of work which is the key factor. In their automatic assumption that women are not suited to and would not wish to be involved in construction work, self-build schemes are merely reflecting — albeit in a heightened form — the prevalent attitudes of society to what are 'right' and 'wrong' sorts of activities for men and women respectively.

Roland Ashley is only one of many who take the view that the level of skill and brute strength necessary to build a home is relatively slight, especially if the design takes the absence of detailed knowledge into account. 'It is quite practicable for women to be involved. But the attitudes and the approach taken means they are not.'

He points a particular finger at the consultants who commonly set up the schemes, advertise them and select applicants. 'Often, I suspect, they simply aren't interested in having women in the scheme and that comes across, creating a very off-putting impression for any women who might be interested in becoming involved.'

Certainly, some such consultants do have rigid ideas about how schemes should be structured and what the role of women in them should be. They insist that they do not deliberately exclude women, but they also make it clear that they do not consider them likely to be able to play a full role. Sometimes they even actively take steps which effectively — if not deliberately — discourage women from going through with an initial application.

'Lets face it,' observed one, 'even where women do take part, it's often a man who ends up doing the work.' The grounds for his belief, however, appeared somewhat tenuous as he could only think of two instances in schemes run by his company, in which a woman had been a member.

As it turned out this was understandable. 'As most women are not qualified,' he continued, 'the only way they will get on a scheme is if they become a labourer and do all the hard work — or if they provide administrative support by acting as secretary.'

Women, he added, were 'definitely not precluded' from applying — but they often didn't realise how heavy and dirty the job would be, so 'more often than not if a woman applies I'll ring her up to see if she realises the amount of messy, dirty, heavy work involved.'

Women in self-build

With such encouragement, it is hardly surprising that most women then beat a hasty retreat. Yet there is evidence that if given a supportive and encouraging atmosphere in which to work, women are no more reluctant to get their hands dirty, and no less capable of dealing with physically strenuous tasks than men.

Southampton-based *Constructive Individuals*, was set up by a group of five

...When a woman applies I ring her up to see if she realises the amount of dirty, messy, heavy work involved...

people, including an architect and a builder. CI runs three-week training courses for up to around 18 people, during which the trainees complete the construction of a timber-framed property. The house in question may be commissioned by a client or a speculative proposition for CI.

But what marks the company out is a radically and deliberately different underlying approach from that which normally pervades a self-build scheme. Phil Bixby, one of the founders, describes it as being about 'demystifying the building process and challenging peoples' preconceptions of what they can and can't do.'

The success of this approach, he says, is the speed and competence with which trainees who often lack even basic DIY experience, learn the techniques necessary to complete a home.

'It proves what ordinary, unskilled people can achieve given simple appropriate building designs,' he argues. Work on site is highly organised; trainees receive a brief explanation of the theory and then work it through in practice — usually in small groups. A skilled worker — a plumber or electrician for example — will often show the way and provide guidance, but central to the concept is that trainees who have mastered a skill then pass it on to other trainees.

This non-competitive, yet disciplined, atmosphere appears especially attractive to women. Indeed, women are actively encouraged: 'It is a help in demolishing those preconceptions about what each person is able to do on site. The men and women both come to realise that very little building work is actually about brute strength, and that the techniques involved are actually not that complicated,' says Phil.

The different climate, variously described by participants as being primarily about 'building confidence' and 'making you believe you can do it, which is half the battle' has proved particularly appealing to women. Still in its early days — at the time of writing the group had completed only three projects — the company receives nearly as many applications for places from women as from men. And on two of the three courses so far, women and men were present in equal numbers — including a former ballet dancer in her 60s now renovating her own tumble-down cottage in Italy.

A central element in the CI approach is the use of timber-frame building techniques. Another woman to complete a CI course, Wendy Sunney, observed: 'This timber-frame style of working certainly helps. It doesn't require quite the same degree of skills or, possibly, physical strength, as a brick built property using wet trades would do.' That, though, as she notes, helps all the novices on the course — not just women.

It is a refrain also taken up by the architect Jon Broome, a longstanding advocate of the Walter Segal method of timber-frame self-build housing. Writing in *Housing Review*, the magazine of the Housing Centre Trust, he points out that

Women in self-build

Woodwork teacher and CI trainee, Gerry Henderson, was one of three women on a course at Hindhead, Surrey. Here she is working on site with trainee Michael Wright.

'the conventional self-build framework in this country has been fashioned for "can do" people who by and large will be able to get what they want in housing as they do in other matters'. The result, he concludes, is that a great many people — 'women, elderly people, young people, unemployed people, those without access to loan facilities, those on low incomes, people without building experience (the bulk of the population in other words) — are excluded'.

The Segal method of construction is based on a post and beam timber frame. It does away with the need for wet trades such as bricklaying and plastering while materials such as plasterboard and woodwool slabs are usually lightweight. Schemes using the Segal self-build method have included as active participants the retired, a single mother and the unemployed — a number of whom were subsequently able to use the skills they learned to find work.

But as Jon Broome stresses, schemes challenged the accepted norms. Getting a scheme involving the unemployed off the ground, for example, meant the Housing Corporation had to bend its rules (which insist that a certain proportion of the members of a scheme are skilled). Social security officers had to make a generous interpretation of the benefit rules on 'income' and a building society lent outside its usual rules on income requirements. Add to that the social norms which dictate that only certain types of activity are acceptable and the task facing equal opportunity self-build schemes would appear considerable.

Nevertheless, for women who would like to be actively involved in self-build schemes, 'opting in' to the current mainstream self-build system looks a difficult and unappealing task. Rather, the creation of an alternative movement based on an entirely different and hopefully less exclusive set of premises, appears the way forward.

More information on *Constructive Individuals* in Chapter Twelve.

...Some people even take steps which discourage women from applying to go on self-build schemes...

Any woman who feels at all intimidated at the prospect of joining in with the building work can take encouragement from Doreen Hartley's story. Born and bred in the heart of the Pennines, she knows the true meaning of 'mucking in'. She took a short on-site tea-break to pose for the camera and explain the building work so far...

A formidable lady

When Doreen Hartley says that for a woman to build her own home she must have the patience of Job, the strength of Goliath, and the power of Moses to hold back the sea, she really means it.

And if she's working with a partner, she adds, the relationship must be as solid as a rock.

Mrs Hartley knows what she is talking about. After 20 years of marriage and 11 years of sitting on the perfect plot, she and her husband Ivan are still in the process of building their own house.

It's certainly an impressive team — not the sort where *Mr* digs the foundations and *Mrs* jollies him along bringing tea on a tray — but the more enviable kind of set-up where the two of them work side-by-side, neatly dovetailing together.

At 38, Doreen has been used all her life to strenuous activity. Not that she appreciates this, for having been brought up close to her grandparents' farm and run her own milk round, she takes takes her physical capabilities rather for granted.

Proud, but not boastful, she already has more labouring hours than her husband under her belt. As soon as their nine-year-old has gone to school each morning, Doreen hurriedly climbs into boiler suit and steel toe-capped wellies. 'We're electrical contractors, which means Ivan has got to go whenever the phone rings. I do the books for the business in the evening now which gives me a full day out on site.'

They are building on the site of a former 1930s bungalow on 20 acres of open pasture at the very top of the Pennines. They bought the smallholding 11 years ago to fulfil a lifelong ambition, initially working cattle on it and living in an old weaver's cottage a couple of miles down the road.

The intention behind the cattle was to develop the smallholding to qualify for a Ministry of Agriculture renovation grant to modernise the bungalow. The fact that by the time they had built the herd up to the required number, grants of this type were no longer available, was something of a mixed blessing.

'It was a blow at the time, but it gave us the incentive to take the idea of self-build more seriously. We needed a house that would stand up to the wild conditions we get up here, and one that was cheap to run. I'd seen timber-frame construction during a visit to Canada once, and it left a long-lasting impression.'

Having done her homework, Doreen has no worries about timber-frame construction. 'Mediaeval buildings were all timber-framed and they're still standing. I've visited a lot of timber-frame properties and spoken to the experts, and as I understand it any problems are the result of bad building. Site workers were being careless, breaking the vapour seals, and then not venting them properly. No matter how good your design is, when it comes down to the nitty-gritty you are relying on an intelligent labourer who will take care.'

It was Doreen who gave the decaying bungalow 'a couple of clouts with the digger', cleared the debris, and set about seeking planning permission for another.

Local planning restrictions were an important consideration. In an area of industrial heritage, characterised by its windswept moorland and listed gritstone buildings, new development must be made to blend in. The Hartleys soon learned that traditional features such as mullioned windows and timber guttering must be maintained. Houses must be stone-clad using authentic local stone. External paintwork must be kept subdued — preferably hardwood frames with natural stains. Most important of all was the stipulation that the new house should be built on exactly the same spot as the first.

All this led them towards the *Yorkshire Homes* catalogue offering a range of traditional designs. It was an unfortunate false start. Having waited four years to get the go-ahead to start building the bungalow, the Hartleys were understandably anxious to get their spades deep into the ground.

But no-one could have imagined how deep — for they reached down 15 feet without encountering a single stone. 'It was peat, peat, and more peat,' said Doreen, 'we were sinking into the stuff.'

It meant using proper pile-driving equipment to secure the foundations safely below the peat level. Obviously, it would be more economical to halve the 58sq ft by building on two storeys, reducing their loss to the cost of a redundant set of plans and structural calculations.

Confusion over whether this constituted a planning amendment or a fresh application delayed progress further. By now, Doreen and Ivan had moved into

GORDON WILKINSON

Doreen Hartley taking a quick breather on site

a caravan on site and were busily installing floodlights and temporary shower facilities. Two Christmases later and the caravan was beginning to feel too much like home. But as Doreen stoically points out: 'I'm to live here for the rest of my life, and I want to know from the word go that everything is as right as it's ever going to be. I intend coming out of there in a wooden box.'

The problem with perfectionism, of course, is that you expect everyone else to share the same standards. Doreen is getting what she wants, but not without a certain amount of fighting. She's a formidable lady, fearless both of speaking her mind and playing the dissatisfied customer.

And she does seem to be having an unreasonable amount of complaining to do. Whether it's because of what she calls 'modern day shoddy workmanship', or whether she is over-particular, she has to be admired for her strength of character.

Indeed, where most of us would have long since given up and handed over to the 'expert', Doreen has persevered. To find the best stonemasons in the area — the one and only aspect of the building work she is allowing to be sub-contracted — she toured building sites for days to see other people's work.

When preparing the steel casing for the foundations she worked solidly for three weeks wiring every join by hand. The weekend the concrete was laid and they had machinery on hire, she and Ivan worked relentlessly from Friday through to Sunday evening without any sleep.

When 120 tons of stone arrived, she unloaded every piece herself, measuring and sorting it into different sizes. When faulty goods have been delivered she has taken them apart, loaded them onto her trailer and driven them back to where they came from. She has even had to overcome a dislike of heights to get herself up the scaffolding and onto the roof.

Most of all Doreen enjoys driving the digger. 'A family friend has been helping with the roof trusses and we've got quite a system going. He attaches them, I crane them up, and Ivan's on the roof to receive them.'

As impressive as her tenacity, is her technical knowledge. While it is Ivan who acts as foreman, drawing on his experience on building sites to decide the order of events, Doreen keeps herself informed of all the whys and wherefores. 'I'm not a person who easily sits back. I have to know what's happening and be involved,' she says.

That explains the fluent use of building terms and her enthusiasm for their intended heating system. Following the requirement for economical warmth, the Hartleys' idea of combining maximum insulation with a heat exchanger has caught the attention of the North West Electricity Board.

In fact, Norweb has taken the concept further and come up with an innovative system for Doreen and Ivan to instal.

The design works on the principle that surplus heat from a solid fuel Aga stove can be extracted through its hood to a heat exchanger. Heat and damp from the bathroom, cloakroom and utility room will be extracted through ducts about 4ins wide in the corner of each room, also channelled to the heat exchanger. The exchanger will then act as a refrigerator in reverse — recycling the warm, dry air back into the rooms and keeping a predicted constant heat of 70°F.

Norweb intended to use the house as its 'Medallion 2,000 House Of The Future' for publicity and training purposes. The Hartleys are confident that with the wall and floor insulation, plus the insulation qualities of the Swedish doors they are importing, they will be able to heat the house at an economical rate

Women in self-build

Case study

A big day for the Hartleys as they begin to put up their timber-frame

GORDON WILKINSON

using the Aga alone. Explains Doreen: 'The doors are sandwiched with insulation, and come ready-hung in the frame, so there's none of this sawing a bit off here and planing a bit off there. There will be an open fire in the front room, but this will have a chimney flap installed to stop any heat loss when it isn't being used.'

JS

For Doreen Hartley, working on site has meant overcoming her dislike of heights

Ruth Evans and granddaughter Rebecca, at the back of her unfinished bungalow (see right)

Rod Hackney, President of the Royal Institute of British Architects, firmly believes that women are the real leaders in self-build because they can sustain the pace and take the blows. Nowhere is this better illustrated than in a remarkable mother and daughter team in the Welsh Valleys...

A family affair

When Ruth Evans finally agreed to be moved out of her home from which she had looked out across the Brecon Beacons for 63 years, it was under duress.

Widowed in 1986, it tooks months of persuasion by her massive family to convince her that after a life's worth of coal fires, asbestos walls, draughty windows and a leaking roof, she deserved something better for her eightieth birthday. Even then, it took a firm family promise not to move her too far away before she finally gave in.

Under her daughter's initiative, the family has kept to its word. A teacher in Birmingham, she and her husband took a family-build project on board, constructing a three-bedroomed bungalow between them, less than six feet from the old one.

'They built around me,' explained Mrs Evans, who lived in her decaying home, Broadview, until 11 weeks later, when the new one was ready to move into.

Then, sons, daughters, sons-in-law and grandchildren took the sledge-hammer to Broadview. 'It took two days to knock down,' said grand-daughter Rebecca, 13. 'We started with the roof and worked down.'

With central heating, double glazing, low maintenance UPVC windows, and more space for when the family comes to stay, it is understandable that Mrs Evans has had a change of heart. She is so delighted with modern life — especially the telephone — that she finds it difficult to recall her reluctance.

'When you've lived somewhere for so long it is very upsetting to think that it's all going to be taken away. The view, the garden, the neighbours — I had everything I could wish for there, and I didn't want to leave any of it.'

The self-build package from *Rationalised Building Systems* has given her all this, and more. She selected the design most like her old bungalow, and left RBS to negotiate planning permission for her. She took the company's advice on windows, insulation, and fixtures and fittings, and ordered these by phone as and when the workers were ready.

Mrs Evans has three children, eight grandchildren, and four great-grandchildren. Apart from her son who lives with his family in Canada, the others were all part of the workforce. 'They all pitched in and I was very proud of them,' she said.

It is impressive that none of them had any building experience. They sub-contracted the plumbing and electrical work to experts, but otherwise learnt as they went along.

The bricklaying was done by a 65-year-old local man and his son who reached the roof between them in less than eight weeks. 'He was a good old fellow,' said Mrs Evans, many years his senior. 'I spent all day making them cups of tea.'

The only real delay came at the beginning when it took five weeks to get hold of the steel shuttering needed for the foundations. Mrs Evans remembers it well: 'I wished we'd never bothered at first. Then suddenly it arrived and everything began happening all at once — 124 tons of rubble, two and a half tons of steel, and 138 tons of concrete. There was so much of everything. I thought we were building a fortress.'

Tea-maker was not her only role. Mrs Evans spent her days fetching and carrying whatever she could. Unfortunately, she slipped on the wet clay and broke her wrist which meant that after a short stay in hospital she was out of action for a while.

Once she had moved in and she and Rebecca had begun to decorate, the next important target was a family wedding in the summer. This left seven months to have the bungalow finished and carpeted, and the garden landscaped for when her son comes over from Canada. 'I want it all to look just as it always did,' she said, 'the same familiar surroundings with the same bits of furniture.'

A home that is warmer, dryer, and safer for an elderly lady living alone has surely got to be better?

'Now I've got used to all these mod cons it is. I'm forgetting the other house now, and I'm beginning to see this as my home. This is Broadview.'

JS

11. Community schemes

HRH the Prince of Wales speaking at the official opening of the Rosehaugh self-build housing initiative

Not the monstrous carbuncle

It is now virtually impossible to introduce the subject of self-build community schemes without mentioning Prince Charles within the first sentence.

This is because he once invited various housing experts to a luncheon at Kensington Palace — and made housing for the less privileged the main topic of conversation.

Not that the issue wasn't already under review — long before his presidency of the Royal Institute of Architects, Rod Hackney had acted as prime motivator, not to mention chief cook and bottle washer, on a series of self-help schemes in Macclesfield.

Then there was the prophet of self-build, Walter Segal, who won the support of Labour-controlled Lewisham council when he organised a mixture of people on the council's housing waiting list to build their own street. The houses were consciously frugal — timber-framed, flat roofed, and only a hint of mock-Tudor — and there were only a few of them. But this all served to emphasise the new cause: at last, houses were being built for the ordinary working people, by the ordinary working people, at a price they could well afford.

Such schemes went far to counteract the snobbery and pretension surrounding self-build. It was no longer possible to regard self-build as the suburban hobby for those who liked to keep up with the Jones's and aimed to get rich quick. The self-help philosophy had worthy implications. Self-build activities were starting to swing towards the opposite end of the political pendulum — and, thanks to Prince Charles, it would seem that they still are.

Present at the Royal lunch was Godfrey Bradman, Chairman of the major property group Rosehaugh PLC — and the gathering went on to inspire him to create his well-publicised Tower Hamlets scheme.

For a former tax specialist capable of turning a near bankrupt tea trading company into a high-profile property developer, the prospect of transforming the Prince's request for 'proper homes that the people want' into a reality, was a welcome challenge.

While self-build was the obvious money saver, loans and repayments were less clear. Prince Charles and Godfrey Bradman were talking about homes for low earners, and, of course, the unemployed. Under such circumstances mortgages were out of the question — but it didn't take long for Bradman to interest both the Government, and the Halifax Building Society in an alternative plan.

The Rosehaugh initiative hangs on the commitment of local authorities and other bodies to make land available for self-build without receiving payment for it immediately. Assuming they are willing, the homes are then rented by the self-builders at rents low enough to qualify for housing benefit, with the option for the self-builder tenant to buy the property at some time in the future.

Once all the houses are built, the self-build association is turned into a co-ownership housing association which pays ground rent to whichever body provided the land. It is agreed that if members decide to exercise their right to buy, then the landowner will receive the full price of the land: in short, an attractive, index-linked investment.

Tower Hamlets, East London, is the first scheme of this kind, making the initial indent into a £50m advance from the Halifax, intended eventually to fund 2,000 homes.

The 16 members — selected from 400 applicants — are each experienced in some aspect of building work. Their collective efforts of 26 working hours per person, per week for an expected 18 months have already been praised by Prince Charles on a special Royal visit.

This is not a commercial activity by Rosehaugh, but results from the decision of a company heavily involved in community projects to tackle some of the problems of homelessness and overcrowding in the inner cities. And the key to further success — the next two schemes at the time of writing were to be in Milton Keynes and Islington, London, and there were others in the pipeline —

Community schemes

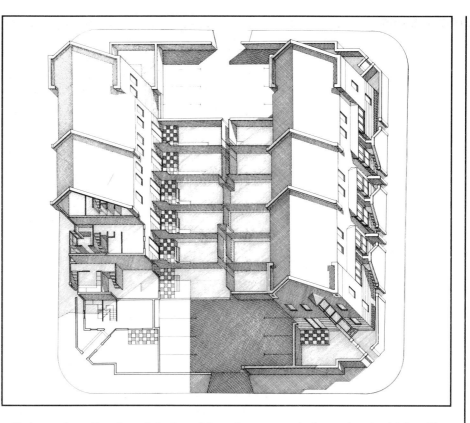

Donbridge Street, Tower Hamlets, London — stage one of the Rosehaugh self-build housing initiative

will depend on Rosehaugh being able to keep rents below a level which will qualify for housing benefit, and the continued support of the Department of Environment and Department of Health Social Security in allowing self-builders to claim unemployment benefit while they are building.

Often passionate, and always ambitious, Godfrey Bradman is hoping to extend his schemes to include long-term prisoners and disadvantaged groups.

He believes that self-build would help both ex-convicts and prisoners back into society by providing them with accommodation, teaching them new skills, and offering an incentive against re-offending.

The implications are far reaching — not least because it would necessitate early release for some prisoners on a day-to-day basis — but the idea is received favourably by the National Association for the Care and Resettlement of Offenders.

Bradman has made public his intention for a scheme designed specially for the handicapped, and talks of the urgency to get 'people living in cardboard boxes in the streets' involved too.

Self-build: a lifeline for urban renewal

Urban self-build schemes are not always about overcoming adversity in the shape of social reform. As a community architect, Rod Hackney is interested in preserving existing neighbourhoods, particularly when threatened with demolition.

'You cannot do self-build on a massive scale,' he says. 'You cannot rush self-build either. I see it as a way of restoring communities and getting people's confidence back. We aim our schemes at the unemployed and they must be given time. It is a social exercise, not a production line.'

This is not a professional viewpoint so much as one based on personal experience. In the late Sixties, Rod Hackney was faced with the prospect of having the house where he lived knocked down. Until, that is, he managed to persuade his neighbours on Black Road that between them they could fight off Macclesfield Council and modernise their homes single-handed.

With that came proof that, when it comes to caring for their environment, the residents do the best job themselves — and the birth of community architecture as we know it.

The refurbishment of those 32 houses on Black Road established the basic principles behind all of Rod Hackney's later schemes: first, that the most effective 'architects' are those who are physically involved in the scheme; second that, ideally, self-builders should know each other beforehand.

This rather goes against the grain of the majority of self-build schemes where potential neighbourhoods are 'created' from a list of applicants.

Rod Hackney does not deny that there is a place for such methods in self-build, but generally the system is not for him. 'I'm not keen on all this manufacturing of groups, with all the rules and fines. If you work with existing communities then there is already an in-built discipline and natural leaders. The way we organise things is that we encourage and cajole. The motivation doesn't come from the fear of being fined. It comes from getting the job done and looking forward to a house at the end of it.'

And getting the job done he certainly does. After Black Road 1 came Black Road 2, 3 and 4. Then there have been self-build schemes involving unemployed council tenants in Manchester, Birmingham, London, and most recently, Stirling.

Combining new development with the renovation of condemned properties, Rod Hackney remains adamant about 'living-in' architects. He recruits recently qualified architects with the flair and the personality to cope with living on site. Jenny Jones, 38, took on a three-year vocation when she moved to the Stirling site to draw up the plans for the renewal of 24 homes, and the erection of seven new ones.

Similarly, as battles for funding and seeking planning permission for 344 houses in the Tunstall area of Stoke-on-Trent hopefully reach their conclusion,

Community schemes

Black Road 2 General Improvement Area: built in 1820; rebuilt by residents in 1979

Right — before improvement work began
Far right — Residents demolish the outside toilets and wash-houses

Right and inset — improvement work included the opening up of dark back alleys to form attractive walled gardens and communal walkways

Rod Hackney sees self-build as the essential lifesaver for urban renewal. 'Take the Stirling situation. There the council is rate-capped and has no money to build houses, but plenty of land. Without self-build that land would continue to lie waste. When we began the scheme, more than 4,000 people were on the housing list. That's a hell of a lot.'

And then there's Tunstall — a General Improvement Area desperately in need of attention. About 25 per cent of the people are out of work and there's a high proportion of elderly.

'Something has to be done doesn't it?' asks Rod Hackney, 'and the point is we can do it through community self-build.'

Prince Charles with Rod Hackney, unveiling a plaque on the Colquhoun Street self-build scheme, Stirling, October 1986

Colquhoun Street with improvement work complete

12. Where to go for help

While it is a fact that, compared with the number of building firms that go bankrupt, self-builders have fewer problems, most admit to things they would do differently another time. MURRAY ARMOR draws on more than 20 years of experience in the self-build world to suggest ways of avoiding mistakes...

Swotting up!

Despite the risks involved, virtually all self-build projects are a great success — mainly because the building societies and banks which provide the finance make sure that they are lending money to those who can demonstrate that they have got everything properly organised and all potential hazards covered by insurances.

Routine inspections by building inspectors and architects, who are to issue the architects' progress certificates required by building societies, guard against further error — as does the determination of self-builders that nothing shall go wrong. Having said this, all self-builders owe it to themselves to swot up as much as they possibly can beforehand. Here are my recommendations:

Building Your Own Home by **Murray Armor**
Published by Ryton Books, £6.95
Available through bookshops, libraries, and by mail from *Ryton Books, 29 Ryton Street, Worksop, Notts. (£8 inc. p&p.)* Essential reading for any self-builder and an ideal companion to *Brick by Brick.*

Build Your Own House by **Stuart Martin**
Now out of print, but available in many libraries. Explains in detail how the author, a college lecturer, built two houses. Deals with building techniques.

Self-builder by **Nicholas Snelgar**
Published by David and Charles, £12.95
Available through bookshops and some libraries. Tells how the author built his own house with all the technical details. Excellent for those building a similar style of house, but otherwise limiting.

Looking for a Mortgage?

LOOK NORTH

Buying a home is the most important purchase you'll ever make. That's why the first thing you should do is **Look North** — you'll find a friendly welcome.

FIRST MORTGAGE?

We know exactly the sort of help and advice you need to make the first move easier. Talk to us and you'll find that **HOMESTART** is just the sort of package you need. Especially with 0.75 per cent off until 30 April, 1990.

FLEXIBLE MORTGAGE PACKAGE?

Whatever home you have your eye on we'll see that you get the right mortgage. With a Flexible Mortgage Package we'll be able to tailor a mortgage to suit your pocket.

£40,000+ MORTGAGE?

If you're after a larger mortgage we've got some good news. With the North of England it'll cost you 0.5 per cent less guaranteed for two years. It's a saving you can't ignore.

 **NORTH OF ENGLAND** BUILDING SOCIETY

Principal Office: Fawcett Street Sunderland SR1 1SA
Telephone (091) 5656272

Mortgage security must be provided. Written information available on request. Interest and discount rates may vary. The Society is regulated in the conduct of its investment business by S.I.B.

The Self-build Manual
Published by the National Federation of Housing Associations, £12.95
Useful manual on legal and other procedures for self-build housing associations. Not relevant to individual self-builders. Federation based at *Warwickgate House, Warwick road, Manchester M16 0DD.*

A Simple Guide to Planning Applications by **Robert Cooke**
Published by Ian Henry Publications, £4.95
A way into and through the labyrinth of planning laws relevant to the self-builder. Revised edition due out March 1989.

Construction Press produces two valuable titles: one on timber-frame housing by the **National House Building Agency**; the other by **Jim Burchell**. Both provide a useful starting point for anyone considering designing and building alone.

Leaflets and magazines

The National and Provincial Building Society produces an excellent leaflet on building your own home. Available free of charge from all regional branches.

The Housing Corporation does a number of leaflets on self-build groups. Available by sending large SAE to *Equity Section, The Housing Corporation, 149 Tottenham Court Road, London W1P 0BN.*

Ryton Books offers its quarterly list **Self-build Opportunities** with details of self-build groups seeking members and new local authority schemes to sell plots to individual self-builders. Issued free of charge to existing customers.

The Self-builder is a magazine for members of self-build groups, produced two or three times a year. Send large SAE and 40p to *Self-builder, Northfield, Snelsins Road, Cleckheaton, W.Yorks, BD19 3UE.*

Courses and conferences

The National and Provincial Building Society covers individual and group self-build. Send large SAE to headquarters at *Provincial House, Bradford, W.Yorks;* **Homesmith Self-build Consultants** cover group self-build only. Send SAE to *Northfield, Snelsins Lane, Cleckheaton, W.Yorks, BD19 3UE.*

Constructive Individuals runs residential courses involving actually building a timber-frame house in 14 days, as well as lectures and demonstrations. Lots of very hard work and basic living. Their trainees love it, but it is pretty tough! Send SAE to *Phil Bixby, 4 Thackray Road, Portswood, Southampton, SO21GT.*

Services to self-builders

There are about a dozen companies offering management services to self-build groups, and an up-to-date list of them is available from the ***National Federation of Housing Associations*** at *Warwickgate House, Warwick Road, Manchester, M16 0DD.* The largest management consultancy is the ***Homesmith Group***, details from them at *Northfield, Snelsins Road, Cleckheaton, W. Yorks, BD19 3UE.* They have branches all over the country. If in any doubt about the standing of a management consultant, ask the National Federation office in Manchester. There is also ***Rother Self-build Consultants*** at *The Old Court House, Hurst Green, Etchingham, Sussex, TN19 7QP.*

If your interest is in individual self-build, there are about a dozen firms offering help in various ways. Virtually all of them advertise in the ***Daily Mail Book of Home Plans,*** which comes out at the *Ideal Home Exhibition* in March each year. Alternatively, it can be bought by mail order from *Plan Publications, 45 Station Road, Redhill, Surrey.*

The best known firms providing architectural services and kits of **traditional materials** to self-builders are:

- ***Design and Materials,*** *Carlton Industrial Estate, Worksop, Notts, S81 9LB*
- ***Rationalised Building Systems Ltd.,*** *Unit 29, Argyll Industrial Estate, Heol-Trelai, Cardiff, South Glamorgan, CF5 5NJ*

Those providing the same service, but in **timber-frame** include:

- ***Prestoplan Ltd.,*** *Stanley Street, Preston, Lancs, PR1 4AT*
- ***Guildway Ltd.,*** *Portsmouth Road, Guildford, Surrey, GU3 1LR*

● *Oliver Homes,* *Burnfoot Industrial Estate, Hawick, Scotland TD9 8SC*
● *Purpose Built Ltd., Spring Lane South, Malvern Link, Worcs. WR14 1AQ*

Books of plans

Home Plans and *Plans for Dream Houses* by *Murray Armor*
Both books gives plans for a range of houses and bungalows — all of which can be built in either traditional materials or timber-frame with sets of plans which can be bought through *Plan Sales Services, Lawn Road, Carlton-in-Lindrick, Worksop, Notts.*
Available from *Ryton Books, Home Plans £11; Plans for Dream Houses, £14 (inc. p&p.)*

● The *Building Bookshop*, London Building Centre, Store Street, Tottenham Court Road, has several American books of plans. They are interesting, but can be very misleading as the plans do not conform to British building regulations.

Technical know-how

There are hundreds of books about DIY building work, and so many new ones keep appearing that any list of them here would soon be out of date. Most are concerned with alterations, renovations or conversions. The best selection of books on building new homes is found in the *Building Bookshop* at the London Building Centre. As well as books, materials and techniques are displayed. Well worth a visit.

NHBC Handbook (*pocket book edition*)
Although self-builders cannot obtain NHBC certificates, the book offers excellent construction guidelines. Ring NHBC publications office on *01 636 3832* for details.

Local authority evening classes
Often one of the best ways of learning new building skills. It is advisable to contact the lecturer beforehand to check that the course is relevant to self-build.

Manufacturers
Manufacturers of building materials are an invaluable source of information, usually in the form of technical booklets about their products. These vary from 200-page books on tiling, such as the ones from *Harley* or *Redland*, to informative leaflets about drain-laying written specially for self-builders by

Hepworth, the drainpipe manufacturers. Most are available from your local builder's merchant, regional building centres, and the national one in *Store Street, London*.

Insurance

Public Liability Insurance: This is the first of three essential insurances and covers you against claims by the general public. For example, if a child trespassing on your site gets hurt, you are liable.

Employer's Liability Insurances: Self-builders have a legal liability to have this type of insurance. Sub-contractors are independent in theory, but if they are injured on site, their solicitors will speedily persuade them that they were actually employees.

Contractor's All Risks Insurance: This deals with everything from theft of materials or tools to malicious or accidental damage, including storm damage. Again, absolutely essential.

Most insurance companies require the self-builder to take out three different policies, but there is a special self-builder's package policy available from the ***Norwich Union*** which covers everything in one document. This is administered by *DMS Services Limited, Orchard House, Blyth, Worksop, Notts.* There is a fixed tariff based on the estimated building costs.